# STORY

# STORYTELLERS

## ANDREW BRANDON

JESUS THROUGH THE EYES OF PEOPLE WHO KNEW HIM

SCRIPTURE UNION
130 CITY ROAD LONDON EC1V 2NJ

© Andrew Brandon 1994

First published 1995

ISBN 0 86201 962 1

Unless otherwise specified, Scripture quotations in this publication are from the Holy Bible, New International Version,
Copyright © 1973, 1978, 1984 International Bible Society,
published by Hodder and Stoughton.

Cover design by Mark Carpenter Design Consultants.
Cover illustration by Matthew Russell.

**British Library Cataloguing–in–Publication Data**
A catalogue record for this book is available from the British
Library.

Phototypeset by Intype, London.
Printed and bound in Great Britain by Cox and Wyman Ltd,
Reading, Berkshire.

# CONTENTS

## Author's note

LUKE 1:26–38

*Mary* wasn't an easy monologue to write. For one thing, I had to disentangle myself from all the popular stereotypes: the queen of heaven, idealised woman, perfect mother, sexless icon and so on. On my first attempt, I placed Mary in a modern setting but it didn't work.

After a lot of frustration, I returned to the first century for my inspiration. Surprisingly, the genealogy was the pivot of the piece, lifting Mary, the country girl, from obscurity and placing her in David's royal family. She was a woman with a sense of history and personal destiny.

The next challenge was to give her a personality and a voice. The *Magnificat* provided me with the clue that I needed. The Mary of the *Magnificat* is a visionary and a poet, a girl who dreams of a Messiah who will tumble tyrants from their thrones. I could hear echoes of the prophets in her words but there was also something very feminine about her language.

# MARY

'My soul praises the Lord,
and my spirit rejoices in God my Saviour,
for he has been mindful
of the humble state of his servant.
From now on all generations
will call me blessed,
for the Mighty One
has done great things for me –
holy is his name.'

We moved from Bethlehem to Nazareth when I was only a child. I have dim memories of the place but they hide in the deep pools of my mind like the shadows of shy fish. Nazareth was a frontier town, a sprawl of houses and streets surrounded by hills sloping down to the plain of Esdraelon.

My family were poor but not without dignity. As soon as I could string sentences together, my father sat me on his knee and taught me our genealogy:

'. . . the son of Heli, the son of Matthat,
the son of Levi. . .'

'These names are like stepping stones,' he said, and stroked my hair tenderly with his fingers. 'They cross the river of time and show us who we are and where we belong. You are not alone, Mary. Learn their names and teach them to your children. The Messiah will come from our family. As the prophet said:

"In those days and at that time
I will make a righteous Branch sprout from David's line;
he will do what is right and just in the land. . .
This is the name by which it will be called:
The Lord our Righteousness." '

Nazareth was full of rumours of the Messiah. 'When he comes,' my father said, 'he will turn the world the right way up and shake out all evil.'

I learnt the genealogy before I had any sense of time or history. Heli, my father, seemed as ageless as Mount Hermon. Adam, Enoch, Abraham and David were more like the relatives who were in and out of our home than figures of antiquity. Nevertheless, their names gave me security. In the twilight between waking and dreaming, I imagined that they gathered around my bed and smiled at me. Later, I learnt their stories. They became no longer 'names' charged with a childish mystery but real people, holding hands across wide fields of history.

Nazareth was full of children. Sometimes I grew tired of

their company and ran to the hills to speak to the older, wiser playmates of my genealogy. David was my favourite. Like me, he was the youngest child in his family and could understand my frustrations. I'd conjure him up in my imagination and say, 'David, my brothers are bullying me. What should I do?' He never replied – the dead cannot hear our voices in the gardens of paradise – but I was comforted by his example.

I chased my dreams across those hills. 'What if I were to be the mother of the Messiah and gave birth to David's greater son,' I thought, and then I'd pretend to hold the child king in my arms. Even in my daydreams he was as heavy as the world and I staggered under his weight.

We were a happy family but times were hard. At night I would pretend to be asleep and listen to my parents' whispered conversations. From these I painted a picture of the world. It was a childish picture, the paint daubed clumsily and the figures disproportionate, but one could still distinguish the reality of the times. Wealthy landlords tossed tenants from their homes for the smallest rent arrears; cold-eyed priests hid their avarice behind a drone of prayer; and, in the background, the tramp, tramp of the legions and Rome's long shadow. Before I understood the words 'poverty' and 'oppression' I felt their meaning, knew instinctively that the wheel of the world wobbled on a broken axle. O, for the coming of the Messiah! In my dreams he galloped across the world on a stallion of starlight and subdued all evil.

My childhood passed quickly, almost too quickly, and I was

suddenly a woman. Dreams dwindled and the world closed in on me demanding surrender and conformity. I was no longer a child chasing dreams across the hills, wind in my face and the scent of flowers filling my nostrils, but a daughter of Israel: a fertile field to be sown with sons and daughters. I accepted the restraints of puberty without protest, but the poetry of wonder lived on. Down in the depths of me I was free. I was Mary, daughter of Abraham, daughter of Judah, daughter of King David, daughter of Heli ... daughter of God. Hallelujah! But only my heart was free. In every other respect I had made my peace with the world and accepted my place in it.

My parents arranged the marriage with Joseph and we were betrothed. I'd come down from the hills of my childhood to a tiny valley cultivated with predictability: marriage, a little house, sons and daughters, old age and then Joseph would pass into genealogy and I'd vanish from memory. Some other girl would rock the Messiah in the cradle of her womb; some other age would see Him. Some other girl from some other age!

And then the angel came, the sunlight crashing on his wings like rivers of light. 'Greetings, Mary,' he said. 'You are highly favoured. The Lord is with you.'

I trembled, shaken by his words.

'You will be with child and give birth to a Son and you are to give him the name Jesus. He will be great and will be called the Son of the Most High. The Lord God will give him the throne of his father David and he will reign over the house of Israel for ever; his kingdom will never end.'

'I am a virgin,' I whispered. 'How will this be?'

'The Holy Spirit will come upon you, and the power of the Most High will overshadow you. So the holy one to be born of you will be called the Son of God... For nothing is impossible with God.'

The light dazzled me. Mother of the Messiah! But even in those first seconds of knowledge, I had an inkling of the cost. A Jewish girl pregnant before marriage! A Son greater than the world! The weight of responsibility! I was joyful – and afraid.

'Let it be done according to your word.' The words stumbled from my lips.

Why was I chosen to be the mother of Christ? I wasn't unique and had no special virtue. I loved God and kept my heart pure for him but so did other girls. Why me? Only one truth rises from the mists. I was chosen because God loves me. He delights to take an ordinary flower and display it at his table.

> 'His mercy extends to those who fear him
> from generation to generation.
> He has performed mighty deeds with his arm;
> he has scattered those who are proud in
> their inmost thoughts.
> He has brought down rulers from their thrones
> but has lifted up the humble.
> He has filled the hungry with good things
> but has sent the rich away empty.
> He has helped his servant Israel,

remembering to be merciful
to Abraham and his descendants for ever,
even as he said to our fathers.'

## Author's note

MATTHEW 1:18–25

After Mary, *Joseph* was a simple assignment: a good man who is suddenly confronted with his fiancée's pregnancy. How will he react?

# JOSEPH

Our engagement was the talk of Nazareth. Local folk had been saying that I should find a wife, and even Dad and Mum were becoming anxious. 'You're getting on, son. All your friends are married and have kids. Isn't there anyone you like? Levi's daughter's still unmarried. What about her?'

'She's a nice girl, Dad, but not my type.' Levi's daughter was no one's type: a face as pinched and mean as a miser's purse, sharp-tongued and as tart as a fresh lemon.

And then Mary appeared. Not that she had been absent, but she suddenly blossomed like a desert crocus after rain. One moment she was a child with long legs and a cloud of unruly hair, and the next, she was a woman with a strong, tender face and beautiful eyes. Her parents often sent her to my workshop on errands. I'd make excuses to keep her there just for the pleasure of listening to her and watching her. I felt as foolish and as clumsy as a school boy, but she seemed to like me.

When we announced our engagement, you should have heard the tongues start to wag. 'He's too old for her! She's only a child! Baby-snatcher! He's old enough to be her father!' I couldn't care less what the townsfolk said. They'd laid siege to my bachelorhood for ten years, pressing their daughters and sisters on me, but I'd held out. My resistance had paid off. I'd found Mary and she loved me, or so I thought. And then she broke the news: 'I'm going to have a baby! God's baby! The Messiah!' I didn't believe her story. Who would? My happiness, my dreams, my identity itself collapsed. I shouted, 'Don't lie to me. Credit me with some intelligence. Who's your lover? Who did this to you?' but inside I felt ... numb ... devastated, a terracotta man shattered by one blow of a hammer. I said what any proud man would have said in the circumstances, but felt detached from myself as if the angry reprimands and sarcasm were spoken by my shadow and not the real me.

I didn't sleep much that night ... didn't feel like it. This supposedly lovely, loyal girl had all the time been making a fool of me. It didn't make sense. In an instant, the world had been wiped clean of colour; the familiar landmarks had been erased; nothing, nothing made sense anymore.

I remember wondering how I would face the next day, and the day after, and the years that stretched ahead. A lifetime seemed so long and lonely without her. I struggled against sleep, but as the stars began to fade into day I was swallowed by it, dragged under and down into its mystery like a man drowning in deep water. And in that dark, troubled sleep, an angel came to me, a vast, shining figure, his dipped wings etched with light, his voice rolling across the world like thunder: 'Joseph, son of David, do not be afraid to take Mary home as your wife, because what is conceived in her is from the Holy Spirit. She will give birth to a son, and you are to give him the name Jesus, because he will save his people from their sins.'

I awoke and it was day. I thought I'd best go and see Mary.

# Author's note

LUKE 2:8–20

*The Storyteller's Night* is a timeless piece. It is loosely set in the first century but draws on Celtic and Eastern mythology for its inspiration. The monologue juxtaposes the fictitious stories of an old shepherd called Ahaz with the angelic announcement of the nativity. This device is supposed to highlight the contrast between myth and the true story of the birth of Christ. How well it succeeds is for you to decide.

# THE STORYTELLER'S NIGHT

It was a perfect storyteller's night. The stars were frosty and bright and the moon hung above us like a burnished shield. The fire was bright and hot, and our shadows lay huge and crouched behind us like a company of sleeping giants. Beyond the circle of the firelight lay the sheep, huddled together for warmth, their damp fleeces steaming in the cold air. Tender pieces of meat, marinated in wine, olive oil, herbs and garlic, sizzled above the red hot embers filling the night with a delicious aroma.

Yes, it was a perfect storyteller's night.

You must never think that we shepherds are empty-headed folk. I have sat on lonely hillsides with only the sheep, the wind and an old shepherd for company, and listened to such wondrous tales that the sky itself became a stage; and on that stage, I saw great oceans and continents, sea monsters, warlords, women as lovely as the stars, street boys who became kings, and kings who changed into dragons at sunset, angels, demons, and even the great throne of God himself – praise to His name! A good story is like a priceless gem: an heirloom that is carefully guarded and then passed on.

It was a perfect storyteller's night. Old Ahaz felt it. He stirred and pulled the blanket round himself against the chill. 'In my youth,' he began, 'there was a merchant sailor who decided that he would sail to the edge of the world.' He paused and looked around him, his eyes as bright as a bird's in the firelight. 'Go on!' we pleaded. Ahaz was a legend in the neighbourhood. He had lived beyond the memory of all but the oldest folk. His stories were treasured like rare pearls. In his long life, he'd been a mercenary, a sailor, a fisherman, a carpenter, the king of a tribe of dwarfs, the slave of a giantess, a hunter of white elephants and other exotic creatures, and had been loved by a queen so beautiful and savage that she ate her paramours when she tired of them. He was the chief of storytellers! There were times when even we shepherds found his stories incredible, but if we found him out in a contradiction, he would rail on us and call us ignorant and stupid: 'You shepherds know nothing except these hills. I've travelled the world. What I'm saying is the truth.' For fear we'd offend him into silence, we never persisted, but our doubts remained.

It was perfect storyteller's night.

Ahaz had come to the climax of his tale. The fire, the sizzling meat, the dark hillside were forgotten. We were sailors riding a giant swell on the edge of the world. His voice held us more firmly than any anchor. ' "Look!" cried the captain, "The rim of the world. The world's end." '

Ahaz's words trembled in the air for a few heartbeats and then fell silent. Even today, I laugh at the memory of it. For as he spoke, a glorious light broke upon us, and burning in the heart of that splendour stood the angel of the Lord. Ahaz, the storyteller, the dragon-slayer, the fearless killer of monsters, the counsellor of kings and sultans, fell beside me on the cold hillside, covering his face in terror. 'Forgive me!' he pleaded. 'I'll never lie to these poor shepherds again, never terrify them with my tales. Never! Never! Never! Oh, mercy, mercy!' His body twitched and trembled against mine like a ewe giving birth to a lamb.

'Do not be afraid,' said the angel. 'I bring you good news of great joy that will be to all people. Today, in the town of David, a Saviour has been born to you; he is Christ the Lord. This will be a sign to you: you will find the baby wrapped in cloths and lying in a manger.'

I looked up and cried out in wonder. The heavens seemed to shake and every star fell from its place in a vast silver shower. Each star became an angel, and each angel stood in column with his neighbour, until the night resembled a sea of rolling, burning waves. And then the angels spoke. What majesty! Their voices rose and roared together like an ocean of joy unleashed upon the world:

> 'Glory to God in the highest
> and on earth peace to men on
> whom his favour rests'

And then the night was dark again: a perfect storyteller's night. The angels vanished, the glory faded slowly from the sky, but one bright star remained to guide us to the manger of the baby king. The greatest story, the story to end all stories, had begun.

## *Author's note*

LUKE 2:1–20

The nativity story translated to North Wales. Dai and his wife own a small hotel in the village. Nothing out of the ordinary ever happens until...

This monologue was orginally written for Tear Fund and is reproduced by kind permission.

# A KING IN MEREDITH'S FIELD

The Census was very good for business but I was wise enough to keep my mouth shut. Pritchard and some of his boys were all for making trouble. 'These Romans,' he said, 'could teach a leech a thing or two about sucking blood.'

It had been a very busy Saturday and Megan and me were just settling down to watch rugby highlights on TV before bed. I'd just put the kettle on for a nice cuppa when the door-bell went. 'I'll get it, Megan,' I said.

I wasn't happy when I opened the door, not happy at all. A young couple stood there. 'What do you want?' I said. The girl was very pregnant. The bump seemed almost as big as she was.

'Could we stay for the . . .'

I could hear the kettle whistling on the gas and cut the man short. 'Haven't you read the sign?' I said. 'No Vacancies.'

'But my wife is pregnant, sir. She needs . . .'

'Look, boyo[1],' I said, 'I don't want to stand here in the cold and discuss the facts of life. If you want to start a family that's your concern but . . .'

The man interrupted me. 'She's having God's baby, sir. The angel said so.'

'Oh, that's different then. God's baby, is it. Oh, I know just the place for you: Meredith's field. It's just down the road there. If you're lucky the cows will be grazing in the top meadow and you'll be able to use the cow-shed. Wonderful view of God's stars . . . wonderful! Goodnight!'

I closed the door. 'God's baby! Whatever next?'

'Who was that, Dai?'

'Nothing to worry about, Megan. Just a young couple wanting bed and breakfast. Now let's make that cuppa. My tongue's as parched as that desert we saw in the travel brochure.'

I didn't mention that the girl was pregnant. I wanted a peaceful end to the evening. Too soft is my Megan. Her heart would drain my wallet quicker than water through a sieve.

Well, later that night I woke up to the sound of singing. Lovely it was! Lovely! I thought the Morriston Orpheus Choir were singing in my dreams, then I heard Megan snoring like the Festiniogg steam train and saw her teeth in the glass on the bedside table. I knew then I was wide awake. When I dream, Megan is always as beautiful as she was when I first saw her: eyes as green as the sea and . . . Oh, never mind. Let's get on with the story. I stuck my head out of the window and there stood Dillwyn and his shepherds. 'That's a lovely tune, Dillwyn,' I said. 'Where did you learn it?'

'An angel taught it me, Dai.' And then he went on with his singing:

> 'Peace on earth,
> good will to men...'

'An angel you say, Dillwyn? The angel wasn't a certain Miss Myvanwy Price, was she? I didn't know she had any musical talents.'

Dillwyn blushed like a coal fire. 'No, no, Dai,' he said. 'We saw angels in the hills. Shone like stars, they did and sang like ... Oh, you should have heard them. Beautiful, it was, beautiful! They said that King Davy's son had been born in our village this night, told us he'll sit on his dad's throne and reign for ever and ever.'

King Davy was our most famous son. A real rags to riches story. He looked after a few sheep in these hills and then became a king, he did. They tell me he was very talented with a harp and wrote some lovely tunes.

'King Davy's son has been born in this village, you say? Have you been drinking, Dillwyn? I've a good mind to speak to your mam[2] and dad.'

'No, no, Dai. Every word I say is truth. Oh, joy to the world. He's come at last. We've seen him, haven't we, boys? He's in that cow-shed in Meredith's field.'

'A king in Meredith's field? You'll be telling me soon there are dragons nesting on Crib Goch.'

25

Well, next thing I know is that a party of foreign gentlemen turn up in my hotel. Swarthy, they were, with flashing eyes, and jolly as a bunch of boys. They smelled of garlic, fiery spices and old books. 'What might I be helping you with, gentlemen?' I said.

'You are most kind, most kindly, sir.' They bowed as if I was important. 'Could you kindly direct us to the residence of the baby king? We've followed his star from the East and we would humbly like to worship him.'

'Followed his star, you say? You'd do better to buy a proper Road Atlas next time. Stars are very unreliable. Now about this baby king. Last time I heard he was holding court in a cow-shed in Meredith's field. Best you go to the pub on the corner there, the 'Shepherd's Harp' they call it, and ask for a Mr Dillwyn Owen. He's quite an authority on the subject and speaks regularly to angels.'

As soon as they'd gone, I heard Megan clear her throat and knew she was building up for a nag. 'Speaks to angels regularly, does he? I thought you said that Mr Dillwyn Owen was barmy?'

'He is! He is! He's barmy, Megan.'

'Then why did you tell those foreign gentlemen to speak to him then?'

'Tourism, Megan! It's good for business.'

Good for business! I've never been so mistaken in my life. Two days later the village was crawling with old Herod's secret police. Nasty fellows and very aggressive. One of them came snooping round my hotel asking questions. 'Have you seen four suspicious-looking foreigners and a baby king?' he asked. 'The baby's very dangerous.'

'Oh, a baby king, you say? Yes, I know about him. You'll find the infant delinquent stirring up trouble in a cow-shed in Meredith's field just down the road there. Be careful, mind! You're likely to bump into a choir of angels.'

I laughed when he left our hotel. 'Megan,' I said, 'these secret policemen would believe that our sheep were terrorists if Herod told them they were. There's more independent thought in this table.'

That was the last time I laughed for a long while.

Gunfire! I heard the crackle of gunfire. It sounded harmless enough, like those jumping-jacks we let off on bonfire night, but there was nothing harmless about the screams that followed it. I can still hear them in my head, raw agony poured into human throats and human voices. When the gunfire stopped, our boys and babes were scattered on the streets like wreckage after a big storm.

We laid the children side by side on the school-room floor. I couldn't believe that such tiny bodies could be so heavy in my arms, heavier than Yr Wyddfa[3] or Cadair Idris, heavy as my heart. Little Gareth and Ivor were still holding hands – we couldn't pull them apart – and their bodies were pock-marked with bullet holes. My mind rejected what I saw. It was too big, too terrible to take in. 'No, not my grandsons . . . No . . . Please no . . . It can't be? There must be another explanation.' I touched their hands, Gareth's and Ivor's. They were coiled together in a knot, brothers to the end ... cold, cold as the slate they lay on. I reached for Megan. 'O my love,' I whispered, 'whatever happened to our boys? The world's gone mad. And all this to catch a baby king. It's well he's gone from our village. He'd have had no boys his own age to play with.'

'You believe in him then?' asked Megan. Her eyes were full of tears and grief choked her voice.

'Maybe I do. You don't kill all the boys in a village to get rid of a silly story, do you?' I looked at the children. 'I hope he really will bring joy to the world, this king born in Meredith's field. I hope he grows up and ends this madness ... hope he makes these deaths mean something.'

[1]'bach' is a more popular word for 'boy' in North Wales but 'boyo' is better known outside Wales.
[2]'mum' is pronounced 'mam'.
[3]'Yr Wyddfa' is the Welsh name for Snowdon.

## Author's note

LUKE 2:25–35

I've always found Simeon an endearing character. I see him as an old man who has never lost the enthusiasm and spontaneity of youth. He is so full of joy and childlike faith that the religious establishment regard him as an eccentric. It is this refusal to compromise and abandon his dream of seeing the Messiah that allows him to transcend old age. At the conclusion of the monologue, he looks forward to the resurrection. 'This world is for the young,' he says, 'but the future, O, the future, is for the young who live forever.'

# THE YOUNG WHO LIVE FOREVER

Look at me! I am Simeon, Simeon the Elder. The Lord has been gracious to me. Eighty-seven years have passed since my mother gave birth to me. I am bent and seasoned like an old olive tree, but the sap of God is in me; his Spirit dances in my heart. Hallelujah! This old body hangs about me like a threadbare coat, but my heart is young and joyful, and soon I will discard this earthly garment and be with him who is forever young, and sing with multitudes of angels. Hosanna to the God of Israel!

The priests find me something of an embarrassment. 'Simeon,' they scold, 'honour your grey head and behave with dignity.' Dignity for a priest is a face as sombre as a funeral procession, as sad as a widow's heart. They remind me of a caravan of camels; heads and noses held high, a gentle swaying as they walk, a slow, unhurried tread that is supposed to denote great sanctity. If that's dignity, let me be a fool, a humble fool, a clown for God!

We old men are supposed to sit and ruminate upon the past, grow fat on memories. Dreams are for the young who live forever; memories are for the old who have no future but the grave. Don't misunderstand me. I'm no stranger to the past. When the first rains fall and it is better to stay indoors, I sit alone and admire the old pictures. I am like a long-sighted man who finds it easier to focus on things that are far off; the present is often blurred and inconsequential. I have few regrets. The Lord has been gracious to me. Twenty-seven years have passed since I laid Rachel in the arms of God, but she is with me still. I see her, feel the warmth and firmness of her skin, hear the gentle cadence of her voice, smell the subtle fragrance of her. The Lord took her, and, in return, made me a promise: I would not die until I saw him who would save Israel and the Gentiles from their sins. And now that I have seen him, I am ready to depart in peace; to look upon the face of him whom I have loved these many years: the Shepherd God of Israel.

I was in the temple court irritating the priests with my joyfulness, telling any pilgrim who would listen to me that Messiah was on his way, when the Spirit whispered: 'Simeon, he has come. Look about you and you will find him.' I turned expecting to see a noble figure, but instead saw a bashful girl with a baby cradled in her arms. 'It is he!' said the Spirit. My old heart took wing and soared like a swallow. I cried out with joy and ran to him, took him from his mother and held him in the crook of my arm. 'What honour to hold the One who made the world and all who dwell upon it!' He was as light as a snowflake, only a baby, but upon him hung the destiny of our world, of all worlds. Never had majesty worn such humble clothing!

'Daughter,' I said, 'this child will turn Israel upside down.

He is born for peace
but violence and lies will follow at his heels.
And a sword will pierce your own heart too.'

I prayed as I held him:

'Lord, let me leave this world in peace
according to your word.
My eyes have seen your Messiah,
a sunrise to the Gentiles
and the glory of your people Israel.'

Yes, I must leave this world at the beginning of his story, but I go in peace. I have no regrets. The Lord has been very gracious to me. The world is for the young and we old men should leave it to them. It is enough for me to know that he has come who will begin a new age in this world. The child will grow to manhood, die and rise again, so that we who have grown old will never die but live in resurrection with his holy angels. This world is for the young, but the future, O, the future, is for the young who live forever.

I go in peace. The best is yet to come.

# Author's note

LUKE 2:36–38

I wrote *Widows*, the story of Hannah (Gk. Anna) the prophetess, several weeks after writing the Simeon monologue. Their stories are almost identical: two old people who meet baby Jesus in the temple.

As I reflected on Hannah's character, I remembered some of the old ladies who impressed me when I was a boy. One in particular came to mind: a formidable woman who was converted during the Welsh revival. She was short and sprightly, wore a bonnet decorated with Bible verses, and sang hymns with the raucous intensity of a blues singer. During worship, her voice would rumble and growl above the rest like an avalanche. In a church that tended to discourage the participation of women, she represented her sex with gusto and daring. If Hannah ever had a modern incarnation it was that Welsh granny.

As a widow, Hannah would have been very vulnerable. She must have had enormous tenacity to overcome male prejudice and be accepted as a prophetess.

# WIDOWS

My name is Anna. You ask me how old I am? You must be a stranger in Jerusalem. My age is a legend that grows with the telling. I was old when Herod laid the first stones of this temple . . . very old! I'm three-quarters dead already, a sinking ship awash with eternity. Hope in God's promise has kept me alive, kept my spirit youthful.

The priests allow me to live in the temple. They tolerate me and some even speak kindly to me and call me 'mother'. The years have whittled me down to this dry stick of skin and bone. My needs are simple: a floor to sleep on, water to drink, a little bread and fruit to eat and days and nights for prayer and loving God.

At the age of twenty-one, I was widowed and childless, twice cursed by God. People ignored me, regarded me as a sinner judged for a secret infidelity. I was pronounced 'guilty' without a trial, without knowledge of my crime. It was this injustice that drove me to question God. Without a husband or sons to give my life meaning, I had to make sense of the world and find a purpose to fill the years. Even in this land of Torah and the prophets, a widow is a dry and fruitless tree.

I'd never thought about God until that time. Certainly, from my earliest years, he'd always been there: a dark and severe shadow spread across the sunlight of my childhood. The men prayed to him in low, sonorous voices and the boys were instructed in his Law, but he appeared to have little time for his daughters. 'It is better,' said the rabbis, 'to burn Torah than teach it to a woman.' The God of Israel was a man's God: a remote, avenging deity, all trumpets and battles and power and honour and thunder and lightning. I didn't think of him as a friend, but as a huge, rumbling volcano, erupting in great bursts of fire and drowning the world in the white-hot lava of his glory.

But when he came to me, he was not like that at all, but a gentle, tender God, touching my heart with his fingertips and whispering love for me: a woman's God and friend of widows.

In my grief, he spoke to me: 'Daughter, you will witness the fulfilment of the promise made to Abraham and all the prophets. In the evening of your life, you will see the rising of the Morning Star ... He who is Israel's hope and the salvation of the Gentiles.'

He called me to be a prophetess.

For eighty-four years, I've searched the faces of the pilgrims for a sign, listened to their gossip for a rumour of the Christ ... always waiting, watching, hoping, longing.

I saw the girl jostled by a crowd of pilgrims. Her face was familiar but I couldn't recall her name or any other details. I remember laughing at myself: 'You old fool, Anna. At a hundred-and-four, you're still dreaming of a daughter.' I sidled through the crowd and studied her curiously. Her eyes were dark and her ears stuck out a little through her hair. Not a perfect face, but honest and as clear as a polished mirror. She was still at that age where ideals shape the world, where good always wins and truth and justice are not merely fine sentiments crushed by reality. Sensing my scrutiny, she turned and caught me with her smile. A cry startled her and she looked down, drawing my eyes with hers. A baby lay in her arms. The world held its breath.

I heard sparrows chirruping in the temple colonnades and wondered if they were angels singing. I took the baby and cradled him against my breast; the words came easily: 'For unto us a child is born, unto us a son is given, and the government shall be upon his shoulder; and his name shall be called . . .'

'He's a boy,' she said, 'and we've called his name . . .'

But I interrupted her: 'Jesus, for he shall save his people from their sins.'

He has come. The Christ has come. Hallelujah! Do you think I'm mad? You do! I can see it in your face. But you're wrong. These are not the mutterings of senility but a hope more certain than the sunrise. He has come, entered our world through a virgin's womb. I have seen him. Here, in this temple, I held the One who'll sit on David's throne.

Keep your eyes and ears open. Emmanuel visits our world, seeking a bride to share his everlasting kingdom.

Do not despise a widow, for without him we're all widows.

# Author's note

MATTHEW 2:1–12

*The One Star* is a short story rather than a monologue. It tells of a merchant who finds a dying Greek traveller in the mountains. The Greek drifts in and out of consciousness and, during moments of lucidity, speaks of his quest for the one star: 'One night a star appeared, a star so large and brilliant it was like a shepherd among the starry flocks of night . . .'

The story is based on an early Christian legend that gave names and nationalities to the magi. One was said to be a Greek. The details in this story are fictitious but its theme is true: the search for God and meaning.

# THE ONE STAR

This is not a traveller's story, brothers, but the truth. We found the man and woman in a high pass of the Himavat. The woman was dead: her dark skin turned grey and her eyes wide and fixed on a point beyond all earthly horizons. The cold had preserved her body, but it was her face that enthralled me. It was strong and regal and so beautiful my old heart ached with longing. If I was an artist and not a merchant, I would sculpt her in stone and give her immortality.

The man was still alive, but death had already cast its mantle over him. His body shook with fever and he cried out in delirium. He gabbled in many languages; some we knew, but many were unknown to us. He was older than the woman by fifteen years or so, but still very handsome. I remember feeling a twinge of jealousy as I looked down at him, but pity quickly drove it away. He must have known he was dying, but he struggled against it manfully. The fever abated slightly. His eyes focused and a hard, bright intelligence shone in them. 'The swamp sickness,' he whispered, and struggled to sit upright. 'My wife is dead ... died ...' His voice trailed off and he shrugged his shoulders: 'Days blur into each other. I have lost all sense of time.' He turned and looked into my face; his eyes smote me like a commandment: 'Bury her and commend her spirit to the God of Israel.'

'Are you a Jew?' I exclaimed in surprise. He seemed amused by my question and smiled at me.

'No! I'm a Greek,' he replied, and in his broken whisper, I could hear the echo of his true voice: a deep, passionate voice with a hint of joy and laughter in it. I understood then why this beautiful woman had followed him to the end of the world and died beside him.

'And your wife?' I asked, my curiosity overcoming me.

'She came from the far south of Bharata Varsha, beyond the Sindhu river, from the Tamilakim.' His voice was sad and heavy with regret. 'This was to be our final journey and then ...' He was silent for a long time and the fever seemed to release its grip on him. The air was chill and sweet with the scent of flowers and the mountains crowded around us like huge, inscrutable Buddhas, their summits lost in cloud and mystic contemplation. The silence was so deep I could hear the fall of a stone in a distant gully, the drip, drip of melting snow and the beat of a wild duck's wings as it paddled the sky above us. Even my servants were silent, crouched on the sparse grass as if frozen into immobility by a sudden frost.

'Where were you going on this final journey?' I asked, but before he could answer, the fever battered into him again and carried him away from me.

'The star! The star!' he cried, 'I can see it,' and his fingers dug into my arm with desperate energy. I struggled to free myself from him, and, in the struggle, tore this ring from his middle finger. Look at it carefully, brothers. It's of ancient craftsmanship, made of the purest gold and the diamond in its centre is the size of a nightingale's egg. Who was this wandering Greek?

My servants buried his wife and I dutifully committed her into the care of the God of the Jews. I've always regarded the Jews as a troublesome, fanatical race and was intrigued by the Greek's attachment to their God.

The fever savaged him for some hours, but with the advent of night, he grew calm. 'I'm cold, so cold,' he whispered, his voice barely audible. 'Death is coming. I feel it like the first blast of winter, chilling my flesh and blood.'

I am a merchant and not a priest. My skill is not the comfort of the dying, but the subtle interplay of words and timing that clinches a deal in my favour. I gave a low sigh to impress the Greek with my reverence and began my prayers. As a trader, I thought it best to reduce the odds of an unhappy hereafter by invoking the names of as many gods as I could remember. Death is a serious business and I did not wish to insult any god by forgetting to mention him.

'Be silent, man! Spare me your mumbo-jumbo and let me die in peace,' he scolded and his voice cracked like a whip.

I was shocked by his blasphemy, but obeyed him.

'Look!' he murmured, 'The night is like a garden sown with stars.' I placed my ear as close to his lips as possible in order to catch his words. 'I will never complete this journey, but it doesn't matter. I have been very fortunate. Into a few short years I have crammed a thousand lifetimes. I have navigated oceans and trekked across distant lands with only the stars to guide me. They have been reliable companions. On such a night as this I saw the one star, a star that grows brighter with the passing of the years until it burns in my memory like a sun.'

'The one star,' I repeated, my curiosity kindled.

He smiled wistfully at me and was silent for a few moments. 'In my youth I was tutored by some of the wisest teachers in the East. They instructed me in wisdom and taught me the names of the stars and constellations. One night a strange star appeared, a star so large and brilliant it was like a shepherd among the starry flocks of night: a guiding star, a portent of the birth of a king. We followed it for many weeks, travelling by night and sleeping by day, until we arrived in Bethl . . .' The Greek's breathing became shallow and his voice petered into silence.

'God of the Jews,' I prayed, 'don't let him die. Let me hear the end of his story.'

His lips moved. I strained to hear him. 'It is dark, darker than midnight . . . The stars are extinguished . . . I can hear singing.'

'What of the star? Tell me, what of the star,' I pleaded.

'It led us to a child, a kingly child: heaven's brightest Star born into our world to give us light. As it is written: "A Star shall come forth from Jacob, and a Sceptre shall arise from Israel." Go and find him and tell . . .' The Greek's face changed and shone with a gentle radiance. 'I can see the star, the one star,' he cried, and his voice was strong and whole again. 'It has been sent to guide me to his kingdom. *I shall see him!*' The mountains awoke and threw back his words in majestic echoes: 'I shall see him . . . I shall see him . . . I shall see him . . .' In the morning, we buried him next to his wife.

It is a strange tale, brothers. My curiosity rages like a deep thirst. I have heard rumours from the land of Judea. I intend to complete the Greek's journey and find his Star. Who will come with me?

# Author's note

LUKE 4:1–13

The idea for *The Game Show Host* came to me in Sunderland. I was travelling in a car with an actor and we were discussing dramatising the temptation of Christ.

'We could present the temptation as a virtual reality game show,' I said.

'A virtual reality game show?'

'Yes!' I said. 'Satan could be the game show host and Jesus his guest. We could do the piece as a rap.' I began to ad-lib:

'Try on these goggles, Jesus./Why don't you feel the buzz?
I'll blow your neuro-circuits/With an overcharge of bliss.'

We brainstormed for the rest of the journey. I scribbled my thoughts on a scrap of paper and stuffed it in my pocket.

On my return to London, I began to work on the monologue. The challenge was to duplicate the temptations without diminishing their theological significance. After a couple of failed attempts, I gave up the idea of doing the piece as a rap. Instead, I used my original rap verse to introduce each temptation.

The monologue moves with frenetic energy and is full of harsh imagery. Satan, as the game show host, is a malevolent figure. He twists the truth and attacks Jesus with a nihilistic cynicism: 'Isn't your favourite hobby watching murders, wars, rapes, famines, pestilence, disasters and earthquakes and doing nothing about them? Sounds like great entertainment. I love satellite TV!'

Welcome to the hottest game show in the universe!

# THE GAME SHOW HOST: MR VIRTUALITY

Welcome, welcome, welcome to the hottest game show in the universe: the Temptation Game. I'm your host for the evening: Mr Virtuality. Don't believe the libel about me. I'm not a liar or a cheat. *I merely rearrange reality to suit myself.* I'm the v-v-v-v-v-virtuality man. And my special guest tonight is Jesus Christ, Son of God.

Thanks for joining me today, Jesus. It's not often I have an anorexic Messiah on my show – forty days since your last dinner. Hey, that's really something!

Your credits are out of this world:

• You stuck the universe together in six days and stuck your feet up on the seventh. While you were having a rest, evolutionists decided you were irrelevant to the universe.

• Isn't your favourite hobby watching murders, wars, rapes, famines, pestilences, disasters and earthquakes and doing nothing about them? Sounds like great entertainment. I love satellite TV!

• You're visiting this planet and hope to be around long enough to save humanity. I hope the Home Office doesn't revoke your visa. They don't like foreigners!

• Your real Father's God, but your mum was called Mary: sweet sixteen and never been kissed. Very original. Does God have the copyright?

Welcome, welcome, welcome to the hottest game show in the universe: the Temptation Game. We can give you everything your heart desires and more:

Try on these goggles, Jesus.
Why don't you feel the buzz?
I'll blow your neuro-circuits
With an overcharge of BLISS.
Reality is what I say;
It's virtual, it's clever,
But one day I can switch it off
And you'll be mine forever.
(*Last two lines said as an aside.*)

Let's start the game with a wild helter-skelter ride of forbidden, delirious, ecstatic pleasure.

You're hungry? Sure you are! Forty days is a long time between meals. This is my fast-food restaurant. Do you like it? Smell the delicious aromas! Drool! Salivate!

(*Mr Virtuality adopts the manner and voice of a waiter.*) Would you like to make your order, sir? Why not indulge in a sixteen ounce sirloin steak, French fries and seasonal vegetables? Or something simple: a bottle of Champagne, a salmon salad and our very own mayonnaise? A dessert, sir? I would recommend our Fantasy Castle: a selection of chocolate, mint, fudge and almond ice-creams, served on succulent layers of strawberries and covered with lashings of chocolate sauce, double cream and nuts . . . An orgy for the taste buds, sir!

(*Mr Virtuality adopts an expression of mock horror.*) I'd forgotten. My sincerest commiserations! The restaurant's not open today. The chef and staff are on holiday. (*Mr Virtuality brightens.*) But then that shouldn't be a problem with your special skills.

Turn these brickettes into burgers
If you really are God's Son.
Come on, Jesus, gorge yourself.
Don't let your killjoy Father interfere and spoil the fun.

Jesus answered, 'It is written: "Man does not live by bread alone, but on every word that comes from the mouth of God." '

All right! All right! You win. Ten points to Jesus. But let's try you in the flight simulator.

Put on these goggles, Jesus.
Why don't you feel the buzz?
I'll blow your neuro-circuits
With an overcharge of BLISS.

First, we need a piece of architecture approved by Prince Charles, preferably religious – how about St Paul's

Cathedral? – and a dome or pinnacle to leap from. *Jump!* Give the city a display of aeronautical acrobatics: vertical climbs, loop the loops, spins, anything you like. Why not blaze your name across the sky in coloured smoke? JESUS . . . SAVIOUR . . . It would be a great publicity stunt.

(*Mr Virtuality adopts the voice of a ground-control operator.*) 'Ground control to low-flying Messiah. Land immediately or you will be destroyed.' (*Mr Virtuality reverts to normal voice.*) Test your Father's word. Try his defensive shield. Go on! He's promised to send a squadron of high-tech angelic fighters to protect you.

*Jump!*

Jesus answered him, 'It is also written: "Do not put the Lord your God to the test." '

All right! All right! Another ten points to Jesus. But now we come to the third and final temptation. Will he win? Will he lose? Or will he be virtualised? Stay with us on the Temptation Game show and find out!

Welcome, welcome, welcome to the hottest game show in the universe: the Temptation Game. I'm your host for the evening: Mr Virtuality. Don't believe the libel about me. I'm not a liar or a cheat:

Reality is what I say;
It's virtual, it's clever,
But one day I can switch it off
And you'll be mine forever.
(*Last two lines said as an aside.*)

Sit on this seat, Jesus. This is your opportunity to hit the jackpot and win the big prize. Forget heaven. . . I can give you heaven on earth. All you have to do is memorise the items as they pass by and repeat them back to me. . . Simple! You have sixty seconds starting from now:

- *Number one*: Eat your heart out, Adolf Hitler! A leather presidential chair and the power to rule every country in the world.

- *Number two*: You'll never have to worry again about paying the mortgage! A selection of visa cards and bank accounts giving you access to unlimited wealth.

- *Number three*: Become a property tycoon! The title deeds on the world's most prestigious stately homes, palaces, castles, monuments . . .

- *Number four*: Every one loves a despot! The adoration of every man, woman and child on earth on the pain of imprisonment, torture and death.

- *Number five*: Bring back the Inquisition. All is forgiven! A highly trained army of secret police to enforce your benevolent will.

- *Number six*: Plunder the world! Every luxury you desire: beautiful women, fast cars, art treasures, music, exquisite food and the patronage of the rich and famous.

- *Number seven*: An embroidered cushion on which to kneel to worship me!

Jesus said to him, 'Away from me Satan. For it is written:

"Worship the Lord your God, and serve him only".'

When the devil had finished all this tempting, he left him until an opportune time.

## Author's note

LUKE 10:38–42; JOHN 11:1–44

Mary and Martha have always intrigued me. They remind me of my own daughters: one intuitive and reflective, the other a whirlwind of activity. Mary handles the contradictions of her experience with simple trust. She responds to tragedy with mysticism. Martha, on the other hand, is too practical and honest to accept mystical answers. She finds the injustice of life very difficult to handle. 'If I were God,' she says, 'I'd make the world more coherent.'

On the day that I wrote this monologue, I woke up feeling belligerent. I was frustrated with people and circumstances. Actors were harassing me for scripts, correspondence was piling up on my desk, engagements demanded sermon preparation, the garden and house needed urgent attention, and to top it all, it was six o'clock in the morning and my daughters were screeching at each other like wild cats in the next bedroom. Life was untidy and I was angry.

Later, when I studied the Bible passages relating to Martha, I had a sudden jolt of insight. Martha hated loose ends, hated the injustice and contradictions of life. Her tendency to cajole and organise was an attempt to impose order on chaos, to tidy her tiny part of the world.

Here was a character I could connect with: a stubborn, kindly woman with a strong sense of fair play and a loathing of humbug and hypocrisy.

# ANGER

Jesus was late and I was angry. He'd always set his watch by his Father's and wasn't interested in any other schedule. I'd sent a message, told him to come as soon as possible, but he was late, too late. Lazarus was dead. I was a mess of emotions, heartbroken and angry at the same time. Tears were the public face of my grief but inside I shrieked at the futility of his death.

I was angry.

I've always been angry, angry at the way I was treated as a woman, angry because no one wanted to marry me, above all angry at the stupidity and injustice of life. I suppose my ability to organise sprang from the desire to force order on chaos, to make my part of the world predictable and safe.

Lazarus had been dead for four days and still the mourners turned up in droves and squatted in our house. The din was terrible: wailing, screaming, inane condolences. I was so mad I'd have slapped the next person who said we'd see Lazarus on the resurrection day. I couldn't wait that long! I had to get out of the house before I suffocated on all the hypocrisy.

I pushed my way through the mourners to the door.

'Where are you going?' they asked.

'Out!'

Several brave souls tried to stop me. 'It's not proper,' they said, 'to leave the house during the period of mourning.'

I couldn't see any point in pretending. . . never have! 'Mourning!' I said. 'Is that what you call it? I thought you were giving your larynxes a work-out. Forgive me! I thought mourning was something you did when you were really heartbroken!'

I slammed the door behind me and took the short cut through the village. I wanted to sit in a field by myself and cry. I wanted the quiet to remember, to thumb through the old photograph albums of memories. He was my brother and I loved him with all my heart. I was angry that only fairy stories have happy endings. Just for a moment I'd thought the Messiah would make a difference, just for a moment, but Lazarus was dead and I'd come down to earth with a bump.

'Jesus is coming, Miss.' I always hated to be called 'Miss'. I glared at the boy. I couldn't remember his name but I recognised him. He was one of the Cohen lads. They never do anything for nothing. I gave him a coin and made sure he earned it. 'Take me to him,' I said. 'Quick! On the double!'

Jesus recognised me from a distance and came to me. I'd have been happier if he'd walked more briskly! I marched straight up to him. 'You're too late,' I said. 'He's dead. If you'd come earlier you could have done something. Didn't you get my message?'

'Lazarus will rise again.'

I held my temper but felt the flames licking at my self-control. I'd expected something more from him, a little sympathy perhaps, but not a cliché.

'I know he will,' I snapped. 'At the resurrection on the last day.'

'If you trust me, Martha, your brother will live and never die. Do you believe me?'

'I believe that you're the Messiah, the Son of God, the one sent into the world,' I said, but that's just about all I believed.

I never doubted him, you see, not even with Lazarus dead. Jesus had lived in our house and shared his life with us. He was the genuine article, all right. You don't have to be a connoisseur to tell the difference between cheap trinkets and the Crown Jewels. What I doubted was his ability to make a difference, his relevance. With Lazarus' death, I'd pushed Jesus out of the real world into an ethereal hereafter. It was the only way I could glue together my belief in him and the rottenness of life.

'Move the stone!' I couldn't believe my ears. Jesus stood in front of the family tomb with his back to the mourners.

'You can't do that,' I protested. 'Lazarus will stink by now. You're four days too late.'

Jesus had been agitated on his way to the tomb. I'd never

seen him like that before. One moment he was crying his eyes out, and in the next, he was crackling with anger. Tears and rage! I couldn't work it out. Maybe our family tragedy represented something else, a picture, a miniature, of the horror of the world. Perhaps, in a little way, I shared his anger and pain. All I know is that for a few minutes I felt very close to him. It didn't last!

'Move the stone.' The mourners tittered with laughter and the local gossips jotted each detail down in their memories, adding a few embellishments of their own. The stone squealed and screeched as it was shoved from the mouth of the tomb. The noise grated on my nerves. I was angry! Lazarus' death was bad enough without full-blown scandal. Four days late and now Jesus was embarrassing us. I was beginning to wish I hadn't sent the message.

'Lazarus, come out!' He hit the mourners with his punchline and they doubled up with laughter. Hypocrites!

A figure shuffled from the gloom of the tomb. 'I can hardly breathe. Help me!'

Silence. The laughter stuck in their throats like fish bones.

'Help me!'

'You heard him,' Jesus said. 'What are you waiting for?'

We'd buried Lazarus in his grave clothes. When he staggered from the tomb, his face and body were swathed in bandages. The mourners stampeded towards him, whooping and cheering in amazement. I freed his face and hugged and kissed him. His skin was warm.

Jesus was late, but not too late. I smiled at him. He seemed to read my thoughts. 'I told you,' he said, 'but you weren't listening.'

The questions didn't go away with Lazarus' resurrection. Why was he sick in the first place? Why did Jesus delay his arrival? Why did he allow us to go through the agony of bereavement? Why was Lazarus raised from the dead? Why his tears and rage? (Do you understand any of it? Neither do I!) If I were God I'd make the world more coherent. As it is, life is crammed with contradictions. I don't find it easy to trust, but I lash myself to one certainty: the argument may seem flawed but I'd stake my life on the integrity of the Chief Witness.

I believe that Jesus is the Messiah, the Son of God.

# Author's note

JOHN 12:1–11; MATTHEW 26:6–13; MARK 14:3–9

In this monologue, perfume is used as a metaphor for Mary's experience of Jesus: 'You see, I'd always associated him with fragrance. When I was near him, I could breathe, breathe deeply without constriction.'

Her love for Jesus is expressed in a very beautiful action: she anoints his head and feet with spikenard perfume and wipes his feet with her hair. Viewed from a modern perspective, this deed is eccentric yet harmless enough, but in the first century it was a deliberate violation of custom. See how Jesus handles Mary and the whinging men.

# PERFUME

I wanted to tell him that I loved him before it was too late. The seasons of his life had passed quickly, so quickly: spring, summer, autumn and now winter. I could feel it. The frost, the shrinking days, the wind whipping the trees bare of leaves. Jerusalem was in ferment. Jesus had humbled the priests too often to escape retribution. Winter was here – a cold, dead season.

I gave the savings of a lifetime for the jar of spikenard. I wanted to tell Jesus I loved him but not with cheap words. You see, I'd always associated him with fragrance. When I was near him, I could breathe, breathe deeply without constriction. The air was saturated with his perfume. I'd always wanted to read the Torah, sing and shout God's praises, but I was suffocated by my gender. With him, I could breathe. He let me sit at his feet and listen to his teaching. He allowed me to be myself.

Jesus reclined on the couch next to my brother Lazarus. The room was heavy with the sweat of men. His head was turned away from me but the guests on the far side of the table saw me slip into the room. As I approached him, their faces stiffened in expressions of curiosity and shock. I was suddenly intimidated and fumbled with the seal on the alabaster jar. Jesus turned and looked at me. Even his smile could not hide the winter in his face. 'Not long now,' I thought. 'His journey's almost over ... almost!' I wanted to cry out, 'I love you! I understand!'

I struggled again with the seal on the spikenard but it was fixed as stubbornly as a nail. Crack! One blow and the neck of the alabaster jar shattered. I leaned over Jesus and splashed the spikenard over his hair, unloosed my own hair and let the tresses fall across my shoulders to my waist. The men were angry and growled their disapproval:

'She disgraces her head.'

'She insults Rabbi Jesus.'

'A woman's hair should be a hidden glory.'

I knelt at Jesus' feet and kissed them, kissed them again and again, washed them with spikenard and wiped them with my hair. He was very still. I pushed the hair from my eyes and looked up at him, dumb with love's eloquence.

The guests chastised me with their glances. The scent of the perfume filled the house and stung them to reprimand.

'What a terrific waste,' they said. 'More than a year's wages thrown away in a moment. The money could have been given to the poor.'

They didn't understand. Love has no price. Jesus understood. 'She's done a beautiful thing to me,' he said. 'The poor will always be with you, but you won't always have me. She has anointed me for my burial.'

Burial! I'd listened to him for hours, listened with my whole being, memorised each change in his face, each inflection of his voice, groped for meanings behind his words. He confirmed my intuition: 'She's anointed me for my burial.' He would go to Jerusalem and die.

Winter shivered in my soul.

Jesus rode into the city on a donkey and the people acclaimed him the Messiah. I waved a palm branch with the rest and shouted, 'Hosanna to the king who comes in the name of the Lord.' A week later he was dead, stabbed by thorns and nails and the rejection of the people. Winter! Winter!

But what a spring! He is risen and I can breathe again. O, I can breathe again, fill my senses with the joy of him. He is alive and the world is full of his fragrance.

## Author's note

MATTHEW 9:2–8; MARK 2:1–12; LUKE 5:18–26

I wasn't quite sure if I should put this monologue in a modern setting. A roof in first century Capernaum and a roof today have only one thing in common: they keep out the rain or should do.

Use your imagination as you read this story. Pretend that this house is one of those converted barns that are so fashionable with well-heeled yuppies: a one-story building with oak beams, wattle and daub, double glazed windows, designer-label furniture and no ceilings anywhere in sight.

This is one monologue I'll never show to my brother. He's a builder!

# CONCRETE

There's nothing I can do, nothing. My body feels as if it's buried in concrete. That's what it's like to be paralysed. I cannot move my legs, my arms, my hands, my head or even my lips. This voice you hear is not my true voice. No, this is the voice of my thoughts, a caged voice. I've been carried to this rooftop by friends. I can hear them working, hear the squeal and scrape of the slates, but I cannot turn my head to look at them. All I can see is the sky, a sun-washed sheet of blue lathered with clouds. Birds soar above me.

I wish . . . I wish I could fly.

The hole in the roof grows larger every moment. I can tell because the sound of the crowd grows with it: first a murmur and then a muffled roar with one voice shouting above the rest. Must be the owner of the house!

'We'll lower you down any moment but you won't be coming up this way. Jesus will see to that. Up here we'll have the best seat in the house for the miracle.' George is deadly serious about Jesus. I can always tell when he's joking – laughter leaks through his voice. Anyone who can fool

George deserves an Oscar. Who is this man?

The world begins to sway. I'm through the roof and descending fast. I'd have preferred a more dignified entrance: a proper lift, not a bed lowered on four ropes. My body's as good as dead but my senses are very clear. Reality is magnified. I can smell the crowd, feel the heat of their packed bodies, even distinguish individual voices. They're watching me. Just for a moment I've upstaged the Messiah!

That man's still shouting. I hope he's not a violent type!

The crowd parts for me and then surges back like a tide, encirling me in a sea of faces. Where is he? Which one's the Messiah? They all look alike to me.

I panic, close my eyes, remember the accident: the rain sloshing on the windscreen, the hum of the wipers and the hypnotic beam of headlights dragging me towards them. Everything else is suspended in silence. I can't remember the impact or the sound of the collision. Suddenly everything around me turned off like a TV, receded to a bright dot and then vanished altogether. When I woke up I was like this: a ghost of a man encased in concrete ... helpless!

I was very angry. My anger wasn't directed at God but against 'chance' or 'fate' – whatever name you want to give it – that unpredictable element in life. I was condemned to utter helplessness and had no power to appeal against the sentence.

The crowd's electric with anticipation. I force my eyes open.

'Son, your sins are forgiven!' The Messiah stands to the left of me, a Messiah with callused hands and worn clothes. I'm old enough to be his dad and he calls me 'son', tells me my sins are forgiven. What does he know about my sins?

His gaze turns from me and arcs across the crowd. 'I know what you're thinking,' he says. 'Why does this fellow talk like this? He's blaspheming. Who can forgive sins but God alone?' His eyes track down his critics. 'Which is easier to say, "Your sins are forgiven" or "Get up and walk"?'

There's no answer. I look up at his face, such an ordinary face, yet it hides something so big it dwarfs the world. He scares me. I want to bury myself so deep he'll never reach me, never see my sins, but I'm trapped in concrete ... helpless!

'But that you may know I have authority to forgive sins ...' Jesus pauses, lets the silence complete the sentence. What next? He looks down at me and his face is full of warmth, genuine warmth. 'Get up and walk!' he says, in a voice so matter-of-fact and ordinary you'd think he was asking for a cup of tea at a corner cafe.

Get up! Walk! Impossible! And yet the impossible happens. Concrete crumbles and I feel as light as air, a bird winging across vast fields of sky. Free!

'Get up and walk!' His words seize me by the hands and haul me to my feet. Am I dreaming? Was the accident a dream? Is this a dream? The Messiah, the crowd, my friends framed in the hole in the roof are frozen into stillness. Reality is held on pause, but only for a moment. Suddenly the crowd is in motion again. They're cheering and I'm dancing and leaping and waving my arms.

*Storytellers*

The owner of the house is still shouting but he's forgotten about the hole in his roof.

I never will.

## Author's note

LUKE 7:11–17

*The Mountain* is the story of the resurrection of a widow's son. She lived in Nain, a village that snuggled around the base of Mount Little Hermon.

The mountain is used as a symbol.

# THE MOUNTAIN

'Could you hug me, Mum?' he said, 'I feel so cold.'

'Yes, Michael. I'll do my best,' and I cradled him in my arms and rocked him as I had when he was a child. I was cold as well, felt as if I'd climbed the top of our mountain and was shivering in the full blast of a winter gale.

'Is it night, Mum?'

'No,' I said. 'It's just after midday.'

'Then why is it dark in here? Where's Dad?'

'He's gone away, Michael.' I couldn't bring myself to say he was dead. The word was too terrible and final.

'Why is it dark?'

'It must be the shadow of the mountain,' I lied. The room was soaked in sunlight.

Michael was silent for a long time. I thought he was sleeping. 'Mum, I wish I could see Dad again. I miss him.'

'So do I.' I was trying to be brave for his sake. He held my hand. I remembered all the other times he'd held it.

Through the window I could see the tip of the mountain stabbing the sky. There was a great stillness as if the world had drowned beneath an ocean of silence. My mind was a blasphemy: 'First my husband, God, and now my son. What are you playing at?' I never thought to challenge his existence. He was as self-evident as the mountain on which our house was built. It was his character I questioned. All the grand ideas about his righteousness and love didn't seem to measure up to reality. I wondered if he was good or merely capricious, a gambler who shook me in his hand like a dice and threw unlucky numbers. I couldn't bear to look at Michael's face, so I looked away to the mountain. As a child it seemed as big as the world. When storms hurled thunder and lightning from the sky, I thought that God descended and held court on its summit. I'd thrown away this idea with all the other bric-a-brac of childhood, but the mountain remained a potent symbol: God's shadow, inscrutable, unchangeable, everlastingly silent in the face of suffering.

'O, God,' I cried, 'have mercy on me. If you are good and loving, spare my son.' At first my prayers were pleas and then they were fists flailing in the face of God. My agony drove me to rage at him. The mountain seemed to topple and crush me to impotence.

'Mum!' Michael's voice brought me back. It was very weak, no more than a breath.

'What is it, darling?' He'd scolded me for calling him 'darling' when he was eleven, but I reverted to the endearment ... couldn't help myself. All the love I'd given him. So much love squandered. What a waste!

'I can't see anything, Mum.' His eyes were blind, as blank and uncomprehending as they'd been nineteen years earlier when the midwife dangled him on my breasts and told me God had given me a son.

I wanted so very much to be strong, to be his mother and stand by him to the end, but my resolve was battered by a hurricane of grief. It howled out of my soul and carried my resistance away in ruins. 'O, darling, don't leave me. Don't go away. I love you.' My fingers dug into his arms and I felt them grow cold and stiff beneath my touch.

I walked before Michael's coffin. The professional mourners followed behind weeping and beating cymbals in a parody of grief. Michael was to be buried in the mountain. It towered above me with the finality of a gravestone. He would be swallowed by it and forgotten, but the mountain would continue: inviolate, silent, immune to the vagaries of humankind.

Jesus seemed to step out of the mountain. I was startled by his serenity and the tenderness of his eyes. In all the sham sorrow of the funeral, his sympathy was true. I had the strangest notion: the mountain had split open and compassion was pouring over me. 'Hallucination! Madness!' I thought and fastened my eyes to his face in desperation.

'Don't cry,' he whispered and walked to Michael's coffin. 'Young man, I say to you, get up.' It was as if the mountain had found a human voice.

Michael sat up.

He began to talk. How like him! He's inherited my love of words and his father's indiscretion. Sometimes his precocious chatter is a nuisance; that day it was poetry... music. I listened as I'd never listened before and laughed with joy.

Jesus gave Michael back to me.

The years have changed and bent me, but the mountain remains. Sometimes I imagine it trembles beneath my feet, and, in the spring, I marvel at its gentleness. Flowers, colourful and coy as shy girls, peep from its fissures and birds court in its crags and buttresses. Yet it is only a shadow ... only a shadow! One day I will climb the mountain and wait on its summit. He will come for me, stepping from the rock as he did when he gave Michael back to me, and take me from the shadow to reality.

God is mysterious ... beautiful, an abyss of darkness warm as the womb, yet he smiles at me with a human face ... the face of Jesus!

*I come!*

## *Author's note*

MATTHEW 9:18–26; MARK 5:21–43; LUKE 8:41–56

*Jairus* is the story of man who has difficulty showing his feelings.

I see him as an entrepreneurial businessman who has risen from humble beginnings.

# JAIRUS

My girl was dying. Jesus had promised to come and see what he could do. 'Don't worry,' he said, 'she'll be okay. Just believe!'

Don't worry! You must be joking! My daughter was just about breathing when I left her and her face was grey. Every time I thought of her, my heart cracked a little bit more and I wanted to cry. I hadn't cried for years, not even when Dad died.

The crowds hemmed him in like bargain hunters on the first day of the January sales. I went through every combination of the 'I'm stuck in a traffic jam and want to blow up the driver in front of me' fantasy. One moment I was the religious guy from the local Synagogue, and in the next, a crazed psycho who wanted to bomb the crowd into kingdom come and drag Jesus away in his black Merc. My daughter was dying. Why was Jesus walking so slowly? Why didn't he get a move on? I wanted to curse and shout at the crowd, tell them to move away, but I had about enough sense to realise you don't win over a rabbi by swearing at his congregation.

Then that woman came, the one who had the nasty female problem that nobody talks about . . . I can't remember her name. You know the one I mean! Always wore lots of cheap perfume. They did a story about her in the Capernaum Times. Had to sell her house to pay her private medical expenses. Homeless! Lived in the park and walked around in a red coat and dirty plimsolls. Remember? Well, she pushed through the crowd and touched his coat . . . was healed right there and then. She was trying to make a fast getaway when Jesus turned on the crowd and said, 'Who touched me?'

'Oh dear,' I thought, 'We're going to be here all night. Goodbye little daughter!' But that woman – whatever her name is – owned up immediately. She was so nervous she could hardly speak. 'Get on with it, woman. My daughter's dying.' I willed her to be as quick as possible, make some sort of dramatic gesture like throwing away her cheap perfume and saying, 'I'll never need this again! Thank you, Jesus.'

I wanted Jesus to keep on walking and talking at the same time . . . no delays. Instead he stood and spoke to her for hours . . . well, it seemed like hours! Why did he have to do a miracle at a time like this? It wouldn't hurt the woman to suffer a little while longer but my daughter was dying. I resented them both. Then a hand touched my shoulder. I'd been expecting it. I wanted to run away. 'She's dead! You don't need to bother Jesus any more. Come home.'

Come home! I was frightened to go home. All my life I'd hidden my feelings . . . played the man. Sarah is dead! Oh, Sarah, Sarah, Sarah. My mind was like a photograph album full of snapshots: Sarah looking at me through the bars of her cot; Sarah splashing in the bath; Sarah in her school uniform; Sarah singing in a choir ... Sarah, Sarah, Sarah. I would never hear her voice again. Kept on remembering the most funny thing: the hair clip she wanted me to buy her. It was too late now ... kept on saying, 'sorry!' I was demolished, blown to pieces; felt I was going to drown in tears, but I couldn't have cared less. My pain was bigger, much bigger than my pride. Oh, Sarah. What a waste! She was my only child.

'What's wrong?' Jesus came very close and looked at me. I wanted to back away, drive a wedge of space between us.

'I'll tell you what's wrong, Rabbi. The world's just ended. My daughter's dead.' And then I was blubbering buckets and I didn't even freeze when he put his arms round me. I wouldn't even let my dad do that!

'Don't worry. She'll be okay, Jairus. Just believe. Trust be!'

Don't worry ... Just believe ... Trust me! You must be joking! My daughter was dead. I didn't believe in God; didn't believe in messiahs; didn't believe in anything any more. I just kept on sobbing and mumbling sentimental stuff like, 'I'll never forget you. I hope you didn't die in pain. Did you think of me in your last moments, whisper, "Good-bye, Dad"? Oh, Sarah, I'll always love you.' It's sort of embarrassing to say this stuff publicly, but that's how it was.

'Let's go home,' he said, and I followed him. I could think of nowhere else to go.

The relatives were there to meet me, all red-eyed and wailing like a bunch of vampires in a low-budget horror movie. Isaac, my half-brother, was playing sentimental songs on the grand piano and crying like a broken water-pipe. He was about as sincere as a politician before a general election. For a moment I was angry: 'Hey, Isaac, have you got some grit behind your contact lenses?' He looked shocked and his eyes dried out instantly.

'You've made me miss a note,' he said and his soft face crinkled up in annoyance. I wanted to punch him in the mouth, punch all of them.

Marg, my sister-in-law, came over from the table and held my hands. She wore lots of rings on her chubby fingers and they felt cold. Big fat tears smudged her mascara and her chins wobbled as she spoke: 'We're so sorry. We'll all miss her. Sarah was a gorgeous girl.'

'You never said that when she was alive, Marg.'

She ignored the sarcasm and pulled me towards the table: 'I just popped round the corner to Leven's Delicatessen, bought a few things. Come and have a little bite to eat. It's past lunch time. It's not good to grieve on an empty stomach. What do you think, Rabbi?'

'I think we should eat later when Sarah wakes up.' Jesus caught them off guard and they cracked up with laughter. It suddenly hit me how phoney they all were and I started to cry again. Sarah deserved more than this.

'Get out!' he said. I looked round in surprise. I'd never heard a rabbi speak like that before. Marg mumbled something about Jesus not being a real rabbi and everybody else looked upset, genuinely upset – Leven's Delicatessen serves the best apple-strudel in the city!

'You heard the Rabbi,' I said. 'Now get out!'

I had to force myself to go into her room. I'd have sooner faced a firing squad. My wife, Mary, had her head on the pillow next to Sarah's and was just looking at her and holding her hand. She hardly noticed me when I came in. The pillow was soaking wet. I bent down and kissed Sarah on the cheek. Her skin was cold and odourless like plastic, but I could smell her hair, a sort of faint, musky scent. I remembered the hairclip and started to bawl again.

My daughter was dead and I didn't know what to do.

Jesus followed me into the room with three of his disciples. The curtains were open and the room was full of light. Sarah would have liked that.

To be honest, I was half expecting Jesus to give a spiel on, 'Why do the innocent suffer?' or a stiff 'Whisky and Tonic' sermonette on the happiness of the hereafter: good bracing stuff followed by long prayers in one of those singsong religious voices they pick up at seminary. Rabbis come into their own at births, weddings, festivals and funerals ... gives them a chance to shine and show off a bit. Jesus dispensed with the formalities, took Sarah's hand – the one my wife wasn't holding – and spoke to her gently as if she could hear him. 'Little girl, I say to you get up.'

I'm still not quite sure what happened. The miracle was like one of those card tricks a conjurer performs, so quick and ordinary you're left wondering, 'How did he do that? Have I missed something?'

Sarah sat up, looked surprised and asked, 'Why are you all here?'

Just for a moment I thought we'd been tricked, that it was an illusion, and then the truth smashed into me like a prop-forward in the Grand Slam. 'You were dead, darling,' I said, 'but you're alive again.' I was so full of wonder I was afraid to touch her. I thought she might melt away like a dream. I just looked and looked into her face and kept on saying, 'I love you!' And then I was crying all over again.

Rabbi Jesus brought us down to earth with a bang: 'Sarah's hungry. You'd better give her something to eat.'

Mary was apologetic: 'I haven't got anything in.'

'Don't worry, Mary,' I said, 'Marg has been to Leven's Delicatessen to buy a few things,' and suddenly we were all crying and laughing and hugging one another at the same time.

Sarah's married now. . . lives round the corner. She has three lovely kids and a big dog called Brutus. She's married to Leven's boy, David. Marg is pleased. She gets a discount at the Delicatessen. I'll always be grateful to Rabbi Jesus. In one day, I made up for a lifetime of not crying, and I'm better for it. It took Sarah's death to break me and make me into a real man. I can show my feelings now without getting embarrassed. I only have one real regret: I wish I could've told my dad how much I loved him.

## Author's note

LUKE 19:1–10

*Digit the Midget* began life as a children's story. I was invited to speak to a crowd of orphans in India. Some were the children of Bombay prostitutes and others had been abandoned on the streets. I love telling stories and I love children so it was a terrific combination.

How was I going to win their attention?

I started a familiar story from an unusual angle: 'As far back as Zach could remember, he thought in numbers, big, glowing numbers that shone in his head like neon signs.'

They were hooked by the opening line. Most of the children were illiterate but they understood the value of numbers . . . they had to if they wanted to survive on the Bombay streets!

The story has grown-up and now it dabbles in 'A' level mathematics, but whenever I read the piece or see it performed, I remember those children.

# DIGIT THE MIDGET

Okay! So you want to know what I'm doing up this tree?

My name's Zacchaeus, but they call me 'Digit the Midget',
the dwarf with a pocket calculator brain. I've always been a
wizard with numbers. Try me! Give me any number, and I'll
divide it, multiply it, differentiate it, integrate it and give you
its exponential fraction and square root in the time it takes
you to say 'logarithm'. Yeah! I'm the inventor of the very
latest disco mega craze: Digital Rap! Wise up! Forget words!
Rap in numbers! Tell her that you love her with some cool
digits:

Thirty-two, twenty-one, forty-seven, fifty-nine,
I'm rappin' in numbers and I'm feeling fine.
Just tell her that you're true
Sixty-two point two,
Divide seven by pi
Cos it's aces high,
And there is no limit
With Digit the Midget.

So you think I climb trees to compensate for my size – a midget who needs a shrink? Well, you're wrong.

I've always lived in a world of numbers: great big glowing numbers like the luminous digits on a clock. They're predictable, mysterious, cold, perfect. They never talk back with funny cracks. You know the sort of thing I mean? 'Hey, microchip, what will IBM give me for your brain after I've knocked it out?' It's not easy being a freak in a world that markets the perfect body. You don't believe me! Have you ever seen a two-foot-six 007 or a dwarf playing the Terminator? If you're a freak, you're an outsider. You may be given pity but you'll rarely meet acceptance. In my world of numbers, I'm just a zero.

Okay! I'll tell you why I'm perched on this branch. I want a bird's-eye view of Jesus ... literally! You can see his gang from here. Impressive isn't it! He was born a pauper but has more drawing power than Princess Di! The cops have stopped the traffic and cleared the road ... for a carpenter!

I'm not a dreamer. Ideals don't survive very long in the free market! I've been around long enough to know that we all share the same gutter, but some of us are better at disguising our origins than others: a talented press officer and some moralising here and there, and you can serve up strychnine as caviar. Everybody has an angle, everybody! Self-interest rules the world, but JC? I don't know what to make of him. He's a definite 'pi': a 3.141592 twenty-two-over-seven mystery number. He heals the sick and doesn't charge a penny; has fantastic media appeal but shuns publicity; is a born leader but has no political ambition. He scares the living daylights out of me.

Every man and woman is born with a price tag and a number, but he's messed up my digital programme like a computer virus. Anyone who believes that the meek will inherit the earth is either a joke or comes from another planet!

Okay! I've told you what I'm doing up this tree. Satisfied? Now scram before you blow my cover.

I hold my breath and stay absolutely still. My heart thumps and clatters like a noisy fax machine. JC's going to pass right beneath me. He looks ordinary enough: no halo, no gold Rolex, no designer-label clothing, no bodyguard. In fact, for a man who claims to be God programmed into a human body, he's a disappointment. He stops, looks up and traps me with his eyes. 'Zach,' he calls, 'I want to come to your house for dinner.'

How does he know my name? I tumble from the tree and stand shaken before him. The faces in the crowd are blurred, but his face is clear, his eyes blistering me like lasers. He opens the door of my red Porsche and relaxes in the passenger seat. He doesn't even have a key! I hesitate, scared he'll destroy my world of numbers. 'What are you waiting for?' he asks, and I climb into the driver's seat beside him.

'I'm glad you're in the "God" business,' I remark, and wonder if he'll start the engine as well.

We arrive. I park the Porsche outside the house, I'm too nervous to risk the gates. He follows me to the front door and waits while I rummage through my pockets for the keys. Panic! I always keep my keys in my left trouser pocket. I try to get a grip of myself, think in numbers, but they're out of my control, following progressions that lead to . . .

*I see it!* 'Hey, you're the big number,' I gasp, 'the horizontal eight, the number of infinity!' He just looks at me and gives a slow smile as if he expects something more. I try to bluff it out, but it's useless. He sees through the sham and touches the crooked, unhappy little man that hides inside. 'Okay! Okay! Let's talk numbers,' I say. 'I'll give half my money to the poor, and if I've defrauded any one I'll . . . I mean, and all those I've defrauded, I'll repay at four hundred per cent interest.'

I find the keys – they were in my left trouser pocket all the time – and open the door. 'Come in,' I say, and suddenly I don't feel guilty and afraid any more.

I'm called Digit the Midget, the dwarf with the pocket calculator brain, but I no longer think of myself as a zero.

## *Author's note*

MATTHEW 26:69–75; MARK 14:66–72; LUKE 22:54–62; JOHN 18:15–18; 25–27

The story of Peter's denial of Christ. His senses are on overload and his world is reduced to a mass of feelings and impressions.

# THE MAN WHO MET HIMSELF

I remember the crackle of the fire, the acrid stench of smoke and my shadow mimicking me on the walls and flagstones of the courtyard. The house of Caiaphas sparkled with lights. The trial of Jesus had started and roars of anger crashed through the shuttered windows and bolted doors, and rolled across Jerusalem.

I wondered what monster had been unleashed in the Sanhedrin.

I fidgeted and stretched my hands towards the fire, but withdrew them instantly. Blood stained my fingers and palms, another man's blood. 'Malchus,' I groaned, and the girl next to me turned and studied my face. I remembered the weight of the sword, the cold hilt pressed in my palm and the blade glittering like fish scales in the torchlight. If my skill had been with weapons, he'd be dead.

Gethsemane was a shipwreck of memories, unconnected, random, strewn across my mind like the flotsam of a dream: the wind groaning in the olives, the dry-bone rattle of crickets, Jesus praying in lonely agony, Judas and his kiss of treachery, and the dry, sickly taste of fear.

I was scared, scared of myself, scared of my shadow, scared of the strangers that gathered about me. I cowered from their eyes like a thief at an identity parade.

I remember, will always remember, the night I met myself.

I have always been a coward, but not the normal kind of coward. When I was a boy, I never ran from a fight. I was short, but not too short, just short enough to be picked on by bigger boys looking for easy glory. I always stood my ground, fought back with vicious fists and furious determination. My cowardice was a secret affair. I was scared of myself. My life was as phoney as vaudeville: different costumes, different make-up; but somewhere under all the junk the real me was hiding, waiting for the right moment to spring out like a jack-in-the-box and squeal: 'Hey, it's me folks! I'm the real Peter. This clown's an impostor.'

I knew all about disguises, knew that the best place to hide was in a crowd. I was Peter the fisherman, Peter the leader, Peter the socialite, Peter the entertainer, but if the real Peter popped up, I'd cram him back in his box and divert attention by putting my mouth on full throttle.

People were my refuge. I hated being alone . . . hated silence! In this courtyard, in this crowd there was no hiding place. I was alone, a fisherman stranded in a foreign port.

Jesus understood me, understood the extent of my loyalty and love, predicted my betrayal. We faced each other across the Passover table. I remember trying to ward off the gentle scrutiny of his eyes. Tough words swaggered from my lips, but panic skulked in my belly and shivered across my skin with the prickle of tiny claws. 'Lord,' I said, 'I'll never forsake you.'

'Peter,' he whispered, 'before the cock crows you will deny me three times.'

I remember the night. I remember a cold jury of watchful stars, silence shrieking in the empty streets but for the whisper of voices and the pitter-patter of feet on secret errands, lamps spilling light into the darkness, firelight glittering in strange eyes, smouldering charcoal red on frightened faces, and the howls and the scorn and the mockery of his trial.

I remember the remorse of my denials.

The girl was still staring at me. I scowled and tried to shake off her eyes, but they were barbed with certainty. I cursed soundlessly, vehemently. 'You are one of his disciples,' she said and raised her voice for the others to hear: 'Here's one of his disciples.'

'Girl, I don't know him,' I retorted. The lie tumbled out by itself. Fear sucked the moisture from my tongue. I tried to speak, to deny all knowledge of Jesus, but the words caught in my throat.

A second denial followed and a third. A voiced heckled me from the shadows of the gate: 'You're one of his disciples.'

'I don't know him,' I protested.

His voice was a soft sneer; 'You're a Galilean. Your accent gives you away.'

'Man, I don't know him . . . I don't know him. I don't know what you're talking about,' I shouted and began to curse and swear. And then the cock crowed, and from the high priest's house, Jesus looked at me. I saw the cockerel, its feathers scorched by the first flames of dawn, and then it vanished, and in its place I saw myself, my true self, rising like a ghost from the flagstones and staggering towards me: a tragic clown, maimed and blinded by my sins and self-deception.

I wept and ran from the courtyard, but behind me I heard the shuffling footsteps of the real Peter, felt the hot reek of his breath on my neck.

I will always remember the night when I met myself.

## *Author's note*

MATTHEW 27:11–31; MARK 15:1–15; LUKE 22:1–71; 23:1–25;
JOHN 18:28–40; 19:1–16

Pilate is stuck in a traffic jam and talks to his wife on his mobile telephone.

The inspiration for Pilate's character came from that endless charade of fakery and evasion – the political interview. Here we have the all too familiar story of a politician who puts expediency before morality and truth.

# CAR TELEPHONE

(*Pilate is speaking to his wife on a car telephone. The trial of Jesus is over and he is on his way home. In the background, the cheers and the roars of the crowd can be heard along with the occasional police siren.*)

Hello! ... Lucia? I'm stuck in a traffic jam. Tiberius should ban these religious festivals. They're incendiary ... a threat to public order ... My motorcyclists are trying to force a path through the crowd, but ... No, I won't be too heavy handed ... you have my word. I wouldn't risk scratching the car! ! ! ... Sorry! ... Just an attempt at humour ... nothing serious! ... Yes, I promise to be on my best behaviour: no ham sandwiches; no stealing temple funds; no massacres.

Speak up! ... I can't hear you, Lucia ... The crowd are chanting again ... You can hear them? I'm not surprised. Tiberius should be able to hear them in Rome. I'm always astonished by their enthusiasm for an unseen God.

You want to know what happened to the young rabbi, Jesus? ... Forget him! He claimed to be a Messiah ... a Messiah of lost causes. (*Pilate adopts the voice and rhetoric of the professional politician.*) Give me a God who looks and behaves like me, a God who understands power and ambition; give me a God who has no scruples of conscience and dares to recreate the world in his image; give me Rome; give me Tiber... Of course I'm evading your question! You're married to a politician! Be patient... I'll talk to you about the young rabbi later... Yes, I know you had a dream about him...

(*Pilate starts to feel uncomfortable.*)

Yes, there was something odd about him... (*Pilate has to think of this quickly.*) He wasn't the usual type of zealot: wild eyed, drunk on patriotism and spewing out prophecies about the end of the world.

Yes, he did fit the character in your dream... Coincidence!... Or have you been taking those sleeping pills again?... No, the little blue ones. Remember what happened last ti... All right, all right, calm down, Lucia! I know you're concerned about my safety, but don't let this Messiah rubbish go to your head. There's only one tribunal that really matters: Caesar's! This Jesus fellow is a Messiah of lost causes. He doesn't count any more... He's...

(*Lucia persists in asking more uncomfortable questions. Pilate is determined to maintain control.*)

... Well, he claimed to be a king, yes... Blasphemy?... Yes, but I don't take any of this 'Son of God' nonsense seriously. Tiberius is supposed to be divine, but do any of us believe it? Of course not! It's the invention of his media department... a brilliant piece of propaganda and good for his ratings in the polls, but he's no more divine than you or me. (*Lucia expresses concern that his comments could be misconstrued as treachery.*) Stop worrying. No one can over-hear us, Lucia. The technical people have fixed the phones. They're not bugged ... not any more ...

Why do I always have to repeat myself? ... Yes, he definitely said he was a king ... Yes, unequivocally, but his kingship was impossible to prove ...

(*Pilate is now thoroughly exasperated, but determined not to show it.*)

Why? Well, he said that his kingdom was not of this world. If he was a normal sort of king, I could hold a full, independent enquiry and verify his claim. But you must agree, it's difficult to track down an 'out of this world' kingdom. Where do you begin looking? The idea's as crazy as this Jewish belief in an unseen God. I can handle ordinary messiahs – I understand their hatred and craving for power – but this rabbi ...

Yes, he scared me ... There! Satisfied! What is this? Female intuition? ... I thought you'd seen it in that dream of yours ... Because he didn't seem to have the imagination to be afraid of me. These Jewish zealots are always scared, but they cover it up with bravado, or else they grovel and weep and plead with me to spare their lives. Either way, they're scared. You can smell their fear; it stares at you from deep in their eyes. The young rabbi was different – a one-off. I've never met his type before. He acted as if he was the judge and I was on trial ... He said that all those on the side of truth listen to him ... No, absolutely not. The only truth I believe is Rome: the power to enforce any version of reality

Caesar chooses.

Yes, he did appear to be sane ... but only in appearance ...
I'll tell you exactly what I mean ... He looked all right, spoke
with assurance, even dignity, but his claims were crazy ... He
looked me straight in the eye and said, 'You would have no
power over me if it were not given you from above' ... An
insignificant rabbi claiming authority over a Roman governor
... over Rome! Can you imagine it! ... You can? ... Look,
don't keep on bringing up this kingship rubbish ... What do
you think he's the king of then? ... *What!* ... *the universe?*
A Jew ... a Nazarene ... a man without Roman citizenship
or links with Caesar ... king of the universe!

(*Pilate laughs the self-satisfied, scornful laugh of the politician
faced with an absurd statement, and then is suddenly serious.*)

Lucia, throw away those blue pills immediately. Forget this
rabbi ... FORGET HIM! He doesn't matter any more ...
He's a Messiah of lost causes. Rome is the only god worth
serving: unlimited power; eternal glor ...

YES! ... All right! *I signed the death warrant*; I crucified
your king of the universe ... Don't you understand? ... I
know he was innocent ... I know! If it makes you feel any
better, I didn't want to crucify him. Curse those Sanhedrin
priests. The young rabbi deserved to live ... Did you hear
me, Lucia? HE DESERVED TO LIVE! Any man who pro-
vokes such jealousy and rage in the Sanhedrin snake pit
deserves to live ... I had no alternative ... I was manipulated
... threatened! 'Pilate,' they hissed, 'if you let this man go,
you're no friend of Caesar's. Anyone who claims to be a
king opposes Caesar.' How could I let an insignificant Jew,

a slave of Rome, stand in the way of my ambition ... our future, Lucia?

Will you listen to me! I was given a choice: Caesar or this Jesus. A Messiah of lost causes, or the might of Rome ... *I know he was innocent.* Don't be naive, Lucia. What does law have to do with justice? The law exists to give Rome a spurious legitimacy. If justice ruled the Empire, the Empire would cease to exist ...

What do I care about justice and truth? Truth is Rome and Rome is truth ... I choose Rome ... Be silent, woman! You're my wife, not my judge. No more questions ... The Messiah is dead. Long live Rome! ... I've washed his blood from my hands; don't stain them again; don't bring him to life with your conscience and superstitious dreams!

*Pilate slams down the phone in disgust.*

*Four years after the crucifixion of Jesus, Pilate is recalled to Rome for the massacre of a group of Samaritan pilgrims. After an audience with the Emperor Gaius, he telephones Lucia from his hotel suite, and leaves a message on her answerphone.*

I wish I could speak to you properly ... Never liked using answerphones ... I'd like to hear your voice one last time ... say goodbye ...

I saw the Emperor Gaius this morning. I'd expected the summons earlier. I'm disgraced. He called me a liability ... said I'd abused my privileges and the power of Rome ... He gave me a phial of poison and said I'd know what to do:

'Rome has no place for you any longer. Better luck with the gods!'

I'll be dead by the time you hear this . . . I'm so sorry! . . . I've mixed the poison in a goblet of wine . . . It's on the table in front of me . . . Strange! Every time I look into it, I see the young rabbi's face. . . Jesus.

(*Pilate pauses and remembers.*) I wonder if he's still interested in lost causes?

## Author's note

MATTHEW 27:57–61; MARK 15:42–47; LUKE 23:50–56; JOHN 19:38–42; JOHN 20:1–18

This is the story of Joseph of Arimathea – a good man who is afraid to stand out. Guilty by silence!

# GUILTY SILENCE

The trial of Jesus was a farce. How do I know? I was there. My name is Joseph and I'm a senior politician in the Pharisaic party. The whips on both sides of the house, Sadducean and Pharisaic, brought the back-benches into line and made sure of the vote. Not that they had to try too hard. Jesus had antagonised most of them already by his public exposé of their hypocrisy. Let's face it, you're hardly going to vote in favour of a man who calls you a 'whitewashed tomb' and dismisses your punctilious Law-keeping as 'straining out a gnat and swallowing a camel'.

They arrested Jesus in our public gardens at Gethsemane. Caiaphas said that a night-sitting of the Sanhedrin would guarantee a full house, but really he was scared of the people. The Sanhedrin had the political power; Jesus had the charisma and crowd appeal. If you want to execute a local hero, you don't hold a public referendum!

Jesus was dragged into the house of Caiaphas surrounded by armed guards and gloating priests. The politicans of the Sanhedrin sat around him in the traditional semicircle. There was nothing benign about the formation. It reminded me of the outstretched paws of a pouncing lion. I was sitting in my usual seat near the centre of the semicircle and could see each face clearly. A politician learns to read the faces of his colleagues and adversaries. A twitch of the eyelid, a tightening of the jaw muscles, a look of panic or incredulity can reveal more than the most ferocious cross-examination. During my long vigils in the house, I've seen all the vices peeping from behind masks of bogus piety. There were a handful of politicians with integrity but they were relegated to the back benches. A career politician is invariably a pragmatist, more concerned with power than principle. Now the masks were off and their faces frightened me: intense, focused, glutted with a greed for righteous blood. Don't be fooled by the Sanhedrin's press department; this was not a trial but a gangland murder.

Caiaphas made a slight gesture with his hand for silence. There was a hush over the Sanhedrin, but it couldn't be described as silence, more the throbbing accumulation of tension before the concussions of an earthquake. Caiaphas' voice sounded shrill in the hostile stillness: 'We've brought you here to examine your teaching. There have been reports that your disciples are renegades who have no respect for the Torah. What have you to say?'

Jesus was silent.

We politicians are not accustomed to silence. We're profligate with words, spend them extravagantly, outdo one another in eloquence and repartee. I watched Jesus through a blur of tears, not the scripted variety one uses after a major catastrophe but spontaneous tears. I willed Jesus to refute the charges and confound his accusers as he'd done so many times before, but he was silent. 'Speak up, man,' I pleaded inwardly. 'Defend yourself!'

As a senior politician, I could have spoken in his defence and salvaged a little honour. Instead my silence condemned him.

The witnesses, if they deserve to be dignified by such a title, were recruited from Jerusalem's low-life riffraff, seedy men with seedy pasts who turned libel into evidence. They were flattered by the attention of the Sanhedrin, flattered by the generous bribes that jangled in their pockets.

'He's a terrorist. I swear it on the holy books. He said he'd blow up the temple and build it himself in three days.'

Caiaphas brought the pantomime to an end: 'What do you say in answer to these serious allegations?'

Jesus was silent.

Caiaphas dimissed the witnesses and put aside any pretence of legality and justice. He asked the only question that really mattered to the Sanhedrin: 'I charge you under oath by the living God: tell us if you're the Christ, the Son of the Blessed One!'

'I am,' said Jesus. 'And you will see the Son of Man sitting at the right hand of the Mighty One and coming on the clouds of heaven.'

Caiaphas ripped his priestly garments. 'Why do we need any more witnesses?' he asked. 'You have heard the blasphemy. What do you think?'

The question was pointless. The verdict was already decided before the trial.

I witnessed a rape of justice and did nothing. Why? I was scared, scared of the loneliness of standing alone, scared of being the odd man out, scared of mockery and laughter, scared of losing my respectability and good name. His trial was the final compromise. His silence condemns me; my silence condemned him.

After his execution, I went staight to the Roman governor and asked for the custody of his body. It was too late to speak out in his defence, but I wanted to be truthful to myself. Jesus was everything I'd ever wanted to be. By denying him, I was denying myself. The dishonesty had to end.

I buried him with honour in my own tomb. It was supposed to be a belated apology for my silence, but it felt more like complicity in the crime. I longed for an opportunity to make amends for my betrayed ideals, my compromise.

Three days later he vacated my tomb and gave me a second chance.

# Author's note

JOHN 20:1–18

*Mirrors* is the story of Mary Magdalene. Throughout Church history she has often been cast as the bad girl opposite the other Mary's alter ego – the virgin queen. This view has been reinforced by Christian art. Often Mary Magdalene pouts from paintings with all the smouldering sexuality of a Marilyn Monroe.

This monologue is both a parody of the classical view of Mary Magdalene and a reflection on self-worth.

*Mirrors* is a mirror for us all.

# MIRRORS

The camera crew have brought me back to this garden. I never had much of a thing for gardens myself. I was more of your street corners, lamp-posts and dingy bedsits sorta girl. My old job was called 'the game'. The game! That's a laugh. I never found it very entertaining: more like roulette with a loaded gun than a harmless game of pool or basketball.

You see, I became a woman of the night 'cause no man would ever want me by day. I've always regarded myself as a freak of nature: Frankenstein's head on Marilyn Monroe's body. Well, that's me. I'm perfect from the neck down, but don't look up! Eddy said: 'I don't mind what you do with your body, girl, but don't show your face round here. It's bad for business!' So I kept my face covered and told my customers it was to protect my privacy. One bloke's curiosity got the better of him and he had a peep. I was in hospital for weeks afterwards!

I've never been a sentimental sorta girl; never had the chance really. No one's ever sent me a Valentine card or handed me a bunch of red roses. When a man says, 'I love women', he don't mean he loves all women, just those who look like the page 3 girl. If a pretty girl falls over in a bar or her car breaks down, men fight each other to help her, but what if she's fat or ugly! ! I was used and abused, then thrown away like an empty beer can. It takes a very special man to love all women equally and treat them as real people. Only one man has ever loved me like that.

When I was a kid, I really hated mirrors; smashed every one in the house. But it didn't make any difference. I could smash mirrors to me heart's content, but meeting people was like walking through a gallery of the things. It really cracked me up. My dad, my mum, teachers, the kids at school, everybody, hurled my reflection back at me, called me 'Dracula's sister', 'Angel face', 'Miss Piggy', 'our ugly little daughter'. That hurt me worst of all. My dad and mum rejected me and blamed me for being ugly. Believe me, there were no gardens and flowers in my childhood, just staring faces and voices lashing me with taunts.

I do go home sometimes to visit my mum – my dad's dead – but I don't really think of it as home. Home is a place of warmth and belonging, but I never remember it like that. I remember it as a prison where I was punished for being ugly. That's all.

He was the first man I ever met whose eyes didn't crawl all over my body like greedy little maggots. Usually men would start with my legs and work up, but he looked me straight in the face and spoke to me as if I really mattered. Before he came, I felt just like a lump of nothing, a blob, but he shaped me into something beautiful. It was really weird. He made me feel fantastic about myself but bad about what I was doing. He looked right inside me and saw everything: the pain, the guilt, the rejection, the demons.

'Mary, your sins are forgiven,' he said and his voice was so deep and tender, I trembled from head to toe. I felt as if I'd been plunged into a lovely warm bath of water and was clean all over, inside as well as outside. I wanted to laugh and sing and cry and dance all at the same time, but ended up just saying, 'Thanks!'

Like I said, I've never been a sentimental sorta girl. I leave the 'dew on the roses' stuff to hymn writers and poets, but this garden's an important place for me. It was here they buried him. I was bawling like a little, lost girl for him, 'cause he'd been crucified by a bunch of religious creeps, and for me, 'cause I was scared I'd be dragged back to the streets and he wouldn't be around to look after me. When he died, I died with him. All the things he'd given me: hope, and the warm, comfy feeling of being accepted and wanted, had gone. I'd come to say a last 'goodbye' and stick some spices on his body, but he weren't there! My life felt as empty as his tomb.

I think he must have been in the garden all the time, just watching me. When he spoke, I knew there was something strange about his voice, but I mistook him for the gardener. The way he spoke was like hearing a song I'd heard many times before, but I couldn't quite get it. Anyway, you don't expect a dead man to talk to you, do you?

'Mary!' That's all he said; that's all he needed to say. For a few wild heartbeats, my name seemed to hang in the air between us and then I was running to him with my arms wide open. 'Mary!' That's all he said, but he did far more than call me. He gave me back my name; took the broken pieces of my life and stuck them back together. He's amazing!

I don't know how to end my story. I could say romantic stuff like, 'He made my heart into his garden and sees me as his lovely flower,' or 'I no longer think of myself as ugly 'cause he's shown me I'm beautiful within,' but it sounds a bit false: all trick photography and hype. I really don't like being ugly and never will, but I'm not afraid of mirrors any more.

## *Author's note*

JOHN 20:24–29

Thomas time-travels very well. He is a modern man struggling for meaning and purpose. Jesus is the last splutter of idealism before the cynicism of middle-age sets in for good.

# MAGIC CORNERS

I was older than the rest of the disciples. They nicknamed me, 'Doubting Thomas', because I adopted a more rational approach to life and wasn't carried along by youthful enthusiasms. Those fisherman needed an academic to keep them on an even keel!

Jesus was the last splutter of idealism before the cynicism of middle age set in for good. Before he called me, I was just getting accustomed to the idea that there were no magic corners in the world. Admittedly, I had times of nostalgia when I longed for the simplicity of childhood. Things were so uncomplicated then. Wardrobes opened into magic countries; Father Christmas shrank his jovial girth to the size of a chimney, even when chimneys were anachronisms stranded on rooftops; elves danced in dark hollows or shaded coppices; and the world was as big as dreams and cluttered with magic corners.

My childhood passed in a blur and soon the slow, creeping cold began and filled in those magic places with deep drifts of snow. Elves and dragons were thrown aside in favour of more adult fantasies:

Money is the Fairy Godmother who can make Cinderella's dreams come true.

A car is the Genie in the Lamp who can turn the wimpish youth into a virile Casanova.

The list goes on and on.

Jesus made me feel young again, young and alive. His kingdom tingled in my senses and uncovered the magic corners of my boyhood. His kingdom belonged to children. When he was murdered, the walls of the world closed in on me again. I felt a sharp jolt, a feeling of dysfunction, as if my three years with Jesus had been a virtual-reality simulation and now I'd stepped back into the real universe.

Three days later, when Peter and John and the others told me he'd risen from the dead and had appeared to them, I was too sad to laugh or argue. Even if Jesus was an impostor and his miracle and kingdom stories had been brilliant fabrications, I would still have been in love with the idea; not as reality, you understand, but as a great work of imaginative fiction akin to *War and Peace*, *The Iliad* or *The Lord of the Rings*. With Jesus' death, I finally came to terms with my predicament. I was alone ... alone, shipwrecked on a tiny world surrounded by the immensity of space. If I were to survive – and I wasn't sure if I wanted to – I'd have to make the best of a bad job and salvage some meaning from the mess. My friends' insistence that Jesus was alive only served to strengthen my resolve. I'd been duped once, allowed myself to believe in magic corners, but never, never again. 'I want proof,' I said, 'tangible proof. Unless I can see the nail marks in his hands and put my finger where the nails were, and put my hand into his side, I will not believe.'

He came when reason and logic had ousted him from the universe along with all the other relics of my childhood. I'd accepted the sentence of unbelief and braced myself for a long exile of despair. I was sitting with the disciples, the odd man out, when he appeared to me. 'Shalom!' he said, and looked so relaxed and ordinary I thought for a moment I'd dozed off and was dreaming. It was his scarred hands that pulled me back to reality. I don't want to sound melodramatic and dress the story up with angelic choirs, heavenly bugles and a thousand-laser light show of revelation. Truth doesn't need a lot of adjectives to prop it up. He was there, filling the space in front of me as undeniably as a mountain.

'Thomas,' he said and reached out his arms, 'put your finger here; see my hands. Reach out your hand and put it into my side. Stop doubting and believe.'

I forgot all about my dignity, fell at his feet, seized his ankles and cried out: 'My Lord and my God!' When I recounted the incident to the chancellor of my university, he merely commented, 'Don't you think you overdid it, Tom? A courteous hand shake and a polite "Welcome back, sir," would have been quite adequate.'

Shake his hand! ! Jesus was alive and the world came to life again. He'd risen from the dead and torn a huge hole in the fabric of the cosmos. Heaven was pouring into the world. Shake his hand!

My colleagues at the university are perplexed by my faith in

Jesus and imagine that I've reverted to a second childhood. 'You should grow up, Tom,' they advise. 'Accept the world for what it is. Fill in the magic corners.' But if by growing up they mean a timidity of mind and spirit that taints all ideals and dreams with cynicism, then long live the child. Let me grow old climbing trees and chasing fireflies on bright, crisp mornings. Let me be a child of his kingdom, dreaming the big dreams of a new age where truth and justice triumph over wrong.

## Author's note

REVELATION 1:9

*Ferryman* is the story of Domitian's tutor. The tutor has fallen out of favour with the Emperor and is exiled to Patmos. The apostle John is the ferryman who takes him to the prison island.

The idea for the story occurred to me during a short ferry trip in Cornwall. The ferryman sat in his boat with one arm resting on the tiller. I sketched his face in my memory: nose slightly too large, skin grooved like an old table and stained mahogany brown, eyes bright, a young man's eyes in an old man's face. To top it all, it was evening and the sky resembled an artist's palette. I turned to my friends and family and exclaimed, 'Ferryman . . . Wow!'

The incentive to write the story came six months later. A friend called Adam was drowned in a boating accident. He was sailing to Australia when his catamaran capsized in the Bay of Biscay. His body was never recovered. For several weeks after the accident, my mind was full of sea, sky, waves, winds and thoughts of the transcience of life.

This story is for you, Adam.

# FERRYMAN

I shuffled along the last mile to Miletus, my body weary and my mind numbed by the shock of exile. I could see the harbour bristling with ships and boats, masts swaying in the gentle swell, hear the squawk of the gulls, and smell the damp, salt sweat of the sea. I have always loved the ocean; thought of it as friend; sought its solace and listened to the deep counsel of its voice; watched it for hours, awed by its intractability and power. Now the sea was to become my prison, its wide walls sealing me in the crypt of Patmos. Domitian, my pupil, had turned against me. As his tutor, I had poured my best years into him, emptied all my learning into his life, and now this . . . !

I had no sons to follow me, to bear my name into the future. He was my son . . . Domitian! He carried the seed of my ideas in his heart, and with these, or so I had thought, he would fertilise the world. I had given birth to an Emperor, a god to replace the fickle breed that inhabit the heaven of myth and human imagination. Knowledge made a fool of me!

The ship was small for such a voyage. Patmos lay beyond the point where the grey, bruised sky vanished into the sea.

Trickles of sunshine splashed through the clouds and lay across the ocean in pools of light. The ferryman sat in the bows, motionless as a hawk. His face and body were scorched and pitted like cracked earth, criss-crossed with the lacerations of the whip, and his wrists still bore the chafing scars of manacles. He was courteous and helped me to a bench that spanned the width of the boat. I remember being startled by his smile. It was not the usual parody of old men, a false grin stretched across a lifetime of compromise and disappointment, but warm, engaging. I was intrigued. Only the very brave smile on the edge of death; the rest of us cower back and hide in memories and illusion.

'Sit here,' he said, 'or would you prefer to lie down and sleep?' He spoke Greek perfectly, but his accent betrayed his country of origin.

'You're a Jew!' I had dealt with Jews before, a subtle race who take their religion very seriously.

He smiled, the same young smile on an old face. 'Yes, I am a Jew. My name is John. I was exiled to Patmos for believing the word of God and the testimony of Jesus.' He spoke carefully as if each word was infinitely valuable.

As we cleared the harbour, the sail scooped the wind and billowed out and the boat surged forward, its prow set firm towards the west. I had read the reports on these followers of Jesus: a dangerous bunch of subversives who predicted the world would end in a storm of fire. Their god was no more than a simple carpenter, crucified for insurrection by our Roman procurator, Pontius Pilate. Spies had reported that they ate the flesh and drank the blood of their god every

Sunday. Even a Rome gorged on pleasure and perversion balked at this distasteful practice. Yet this Jew seemed harmless enough. I watched him for a few moments, felt the stillness emanating from him, and envied his composure: an old ferryman becalmed in a sea of peace.

'What is the attraction of a dead god?' I asked.

He looked at me properly for the first time. His eyes blazed. He seemed to see through me to a kingdom aflame with splendour. I blinked and scolded myself: 'You old clown! Fatigue has made a fool of you. Poetry and deprivation have addled your brains. Pull yourself together. He's merely the ferryman, not an angel.'

'My God is not dead,' replied the ferryman. 'He is alive!' When I dared to look at him again, I saw heaven shining in his face.

'Alive!' I exclaimed. 'How can he be alive? I've read the reports. He was crucified by our proconsul.'

You must understand: I had built my house carefully – tidied the cosmos into neat drawers each marked with a different theorem – and defended it from intruders with all the arrogance and flair of the professional philosopher. Here, afloat in a vast solitude of sky and sea and wind, my house began to crumble.

I was expecting the ferryman to counter with an argument, play a game of logic, but his reply threw me off balance. His words, though simple, seemed to rise up out of great depths: 'I know he is alive,' he whispered in a voice charged with a quiet certainty. 'I know! I know! I have seen him, held him with these hands, listened to his voice – the Eternal Life which was with the Father and was revealed to me. He is the living bread that came down from heaven. If a man eats of this bread he will live forever.'

The ferryman told his story without embellishment, and when it was over, I sat for a long time in silence. In the distance I could see the Isle of Patmos rising from the sea. In the west, the sun played its final encore, an eerie blend of notes rising to a crescendo before the final chord sounded and darkness fell. Suddenly Jesus was with me, unseen yet more real than anything in all the world. I felt his eyes searing me and somewhere in the dark, neglected country of my soul, I heard his voice calling: 'I am the light of the world. Whoever follows me will never walk in darkness, but will have the light of life.'

I had always lived in shadow, talked of truth but had hidden from it. Now I saw my vanity and wept. 'Domitian! Domitian! Oh, my son, Domitian!' I sobbed. 'What have I done to you? I gave up wife and children for you, thought to make you great with my learning, a god in human form worthy of Rome's empire. But what is Rome? A blasphemy, a sword shaken in the face of God. And who are you my son, my son, Domitian? A man, a mere man, deranged by power and delusions of godhead. Forgive me! Forgive me! My life has been wasted ... wasted on a dream.'

Patmos was close now, a fist of rock driven out of the sea by the earth's volcanic violence. The ferryman laid a hand on my shoulder and spoke comfortingly: 'Child, Rome and Domitian are the past. A new Emperor summons you; a new

City awaits you – the City of God, the new Jerusalem. The world, the future belong to him. Serve him well and he will not disappoint you.'

I stumbled from the boat and was marched by an armed guard along a narrow path leading inland from the jetty. My legs were stiff from the voyage and I walked unsteadily. 'Move, man! What's holding you? You should be grateful Domitian's spared your head,' grumbled the guard and pushed me forward. I could hear snatches of song, clear, joyful voices soaring towards me, amplified in the island's huge, natural amphitheatres:

> *'Wake up, O sleeper,*
> *rise from the dead*
> *and Christ will shine on you.'*

The guard saw the question in my eyes and spat out the answer:

'Followers of Jesus! The ferryman's work. We've tried to stamp it out, but it doesn't work. Rough 'em up and kill 'em, and they multiply like rats. It's like a virus that thrives on suffering.'

I looked behind me for the last time. The light had faded from the sky. He sat in his boat, his face turned towards me. Darkness and distance blurred his features, but I felt the keen, sharp stab of his eyes. Then, to my astonishment, he stood and called to me across the water, a cry of hope and freedom:

> *'Maranatha! Maranatha!*
> *The Lord comes!'*

And suddenly the island awoke and countless voices returned his benediction:

> *'Maranatha! Maranatha!*
> *Truly the Lord comes quickly!'*

The ferryman had brought me to a colony of brothers . . . I had come home after a lifetime of wondering.